STRUCTURED SYSTEMS DEVELOPMENT

STRUCTURED SYSTEMS DEVELOPMENT

BY KENNETH T. ORR

PREFACE BY J.D. WARNIER

YOURDON Press
New York, New York

Library of Congress Catalog Card Number: 77-885-93

ISBN: 0-917072-08-1

This book was set in Times Roman by YOURDON Press, using a PDP-11/45 running under the UNIX operating system.

CONTENTS

PREFACE

It is a great pleasure for me to introduce this book by Ken Orr. Despite the distance between Topeka and Paris, we have worked a great deal together exchanging letters and information.

I wish for Ken's book a success parallel to that of the projects it will inspire in businesses both in the United States and, I am sure, far beyond its boundaries.

Many business problems are made worse by a rush to solve the problems before they have been correctly diagnosed. Would it not be useful then to be able to better identify problems? The book that you are about to read addresses this question and supplies both the basic knowledge and the principles of its application.

I particularly appreciate Ken's concern for communicating with his reader. I remember once, a very long time ago, having seen a Walt Disney cartoon. There was an owl perched, alone, on a tree. His speech began, "I was talking to myself, and we said to us. . . ." Too many writers resemble Disney's owl. I've tried not to be among them, but I have the feeling that I've not entirely succeeded. Ken has succeeded, as is demonstrated by the fact that, despite my poor command of English, I was able to read his book in one sitting. But I advise the reader that some books are to be read, and reread. To understand this book completely, one must apply what is said, and then read these pages again for answers to the questions raised by the application.

I would like to point out an important problem in the application of the principles and in the use of the tools that are described. I know from experience how difficult it is to change your habits and to alter the basis on which you approach a problem. And when you have made progress with your own prejudices, you then find that your colleagues are still back where you started, so that what now seems simple to you is incomprehensible to them. It then becomes necessary to devote a significant part of your energies to training project teams, supplying the necessary motivation along with the indispensable base of information.

In my view, motivation can only be achieved with a clear definition of the objectives — objectives on both a business and a human level. The primary objective of a business is to organize a well-structured system that answers the needs of management. I fear that too many analysts and programmers still do not give priority to the two essential qualities of systems: reliability and adaptability to changing needs. Performance, both in time and in space for programs and data, is important, but is secondary compared to reliability and adaptability. Businesses grow and develop: Data are fixed. If data are to give the organization the desired information, it must be possible to update file contents. In the same way, obviously, it must be possible to update the logical structure of files and of programs, a requirement apparently less thoroughly studied. The organization of a structured system has, above all, the advantage of making the system adaptable and reliable.

One of the means of achieving reliability (the principle means, as Ken conclusively shows here) is by making it easy for users, analysts, and programmers to communicate with each other. Too many systems meet the specifications laid down by analysts or programmers, without meeting the expectations of the users.

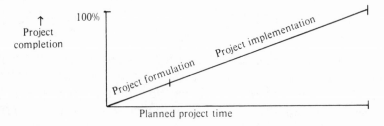

Project schedule.

Finally, the time it takes to formulate a system seems to me to be a very important element in the quality of the system. We recently made some interesting measurements at a large Paris bank. The schedule for the project is represented by the diagram on the preceding page. After training analysts and programmers, our results were:

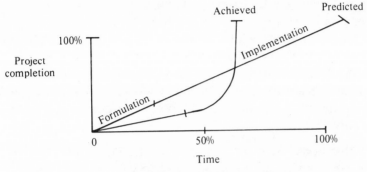

Project results.

Twice as much time was spent in studying the problem, but six times less was spent on its resolution. I should add that doubling the formulation time seriously upset the analysts and programmers involved and their managers even more. We thought after we had consumed 20 percent, and then 40 percent, of the planned project time that we'd have to abandon the project. Only after it became clear toward the end that a much better system was being produced in half the time did the people involved in the project relax.

The two maxims we chose for our group and suggest to you are:

1.   "Take it easy, we're in a hurry."

2.   "If you haven't time now to do it right, will you have time to do it over?"

Reliability, flexibility, and speed of execution are valid business objectives, but are these objectives equally valid for the workers in a business? To the contrary, I believe that it is a dangerous illusion, at this time, to imagine that the objectives of the working man are identical with those of the company.

Man and machine are different; yet why is it that the qualities of the machine are always attributed to man, and those of man to the machine? Man possesses creative imagination, but is subject to error. The machine has no powers of creativity, but is reliable and fast. Certain tools created to solve problems in data processing put the machine before the man, belittling him and making him unhappy, while, at the same time, computer users are seduced into thinking that the machine has some sort of intelligence. These considerations must be kept in mind if one is not to create a group of unsatisfied workers who cannot pursue their objectives of personal development and who do work of poor quality.

In this book, Ken offers tools, but he demands an effort to identify, for a given problem, the tool to use and the manner in which to use it. Thus, he respects man. He knows in what way a project must be carried out so that, in the processing of data, the machine services man — a way that coincides with maximum cost-effectiveness. That is what interests me the most in this book.

Permit me to recommend that the reader pay particular attention to the things that may seem the most simple. The clearest and most self-evident ideas are sometimes the most difficult to assimilate. During a lecture one of my students interrupted with a question: "Is what you're saying completely stupid, or is it so deep I can't understand it?" I could only answer, "Both." Be wary of what appears in this book to be the most elementary and self-evident, for those ideas also are the most important, and the most difficult to absorb.

Paris
November 1976

J.D. Warnier
Professeur á l'Institut Francais
  de Gestion
Section Manager
Data Processing Logic Division
CII Honeywell Bull

FOREWORD

This book is intended for people who are interested in developing solutions to problems, particularly those that employ computer technology. In a manner of speaking, this is the book I wish I'd read and followed ten years ago. It is intended to serve as the introduction to a series of books about the science of systems development in various areas. As you read further, you will find this volume as free of reference to specific computers and computer programming languages as possible. Although I occasionally hint at implementing certain problems with recognizable computer languages, my conviction is that problem formulation and program design must first be done at a logical level, as independent of the architecture of any existing computer or computer language as possible.

Too much of the last twenty years has been spent in altering problems to fit tools, especially tools developed for other purposes; in designing computers and computer systems without a clear idea of their intended use; and in developing computer languages to bridge the growing gap between the computer and the problem.

Most of us have found this whole process increasingly difficult to understand, to communicate, and to execute. A large number of new people entering the field have been encouraged to begin writing programs before they could even read or understand good working programs or systems. Not surprisingly, these poorly trained people have often used enormous man and computer resources attempting to cause their idea of a program to function. Fortunately, many of the ill-conceived monstrosities never did! Somewhat akin to adding insult to injury, the computer itself was finally assigned the task of giving us better and better debugging tools, in hopes somehow that the computer could do what we couldn't. On the whole, though, the computer has proved itself a highly overrated tool for debugging programs. Correspondingly, the systems analyst and programmer have become increasingly overpaid in relation to their productivity.

The tools to help us address many of these vexing problems are, at last, becoming available. A quite simple but unique methodology for problem solving only recently has been discovered and is truly worth writing and reading about. We call it *structured systems design,* characterized as problem solving by a process of successive elaboration. Although some have called this technique "top down/structured programming," we prefer our own term until a better one is commonly accepted.[1]

Structured systems design should appeal to readers who are old-timers in the systems field. If nothing else, it represents a return to fundamentals and provides convincing proof of what most of us have had to learn the hard way. Concentration on the shape of the forest always is more productive than worrying about which tree to cut down next — a way of looking at things, by the way, that has always separated the good analyst from the poor one.

Teaching structured systems techniques, however, presents difficulties for both the teacher and the student, because very little in our education or training equips us to deal with problems in a top-down or "hierarchical" fashion. We are taught, wrongly, to begin at the beginning, not at the end. Experienced programmers have always known the futility of coding programs before they were well-defined, but most of us have done it anyway (at least the author did). Upon becoming managers, many disciplined analysts, who would never put the cart before the horse themselves, often do let their subordinates rush into coding. The temptation to do something (even if it is wrong) is simply

---

[1] Other terms, such as hierarchical analysis, modular programming, or functional analysis, recently have begun to appear in programming literature, but unfortunately these phrases don't capture the essence of what we are trying to do.

too great for most of us to overcome without compelling reasons. Structured systems design provides those reasons by holding out the promise of success as a reward.

The bad habits developed by systems personnel over the last twenty years make some of the recommendations in this book more difficult to apply than might be first imagined. For example, experienced people will find here a number of radical recommendations that appear both to restrict arbitrarily the analyst or programmer in terms of how he designs systems and writes programs and, at the same time, to take all the fun out of it. In reality, we have simply changed the emphasis from construction and testing to design. In order to design and construct systems and programs properly, there are overwhelming reasons to insist that the analyst and programmer do certain things in specific ways and to forego other things altogether. Many of you will find this difficult to accept and, therefore, will not adopt our approach outright. Before you judge our recommendations, read the book, work the examples, and apply the process to some real problems. Once you use structured systems design and understand its power, I predict that you never will use any other approach! Perhaps you also will begin to understand, as I myself have only begun to perceive, why systems design has been such a frustrating occupation up to now.

Systems design is a new field with little theoretical basis. Although the last word on systems design clearly has not been written, we have had enough traumatic experiences to know that the old methods simply will not be good enough for the future. The cost of computer hardware has decreased by many orders of magnitude in the last twenty years, yet there have not been similar reductions for software, especially application software. Indeed, things may have gotten worse. Research indicates that structured systems design is beginning to reverse that trend. Its results point to dramatic improvement in all aspects: faster development, greater reliability, less maintenance, and overall intelligibility. In short, with structured systems design techniques we can produce systems and programs not only faster, but better as well.

Although a number of books have appeared recently with structured programming or structured design in the title, these texts, with notable exceptions, incorporated only some of the rules of structured programming into old-fashioned systems or programming texts without fully explaining their implications or how to teach them. Often, the authors have read the letter of the law but missed the spirit. While that may sell textbooks, I cannot recommend this approach. Since structured systems development represents a radical departure from previous methods of systems development, a text dealing with the subject must also employ a new approach (which I have attempted). Thus, I have consciously tried to avoid destructive concessions to the past, either in terms of systems design, programming languages, or computer architecture. Structured systems design requires only that the reader have an open, logical mind and a willingness to try a new way to attack problems.

If you are a beginner, don't be intimidated by the subject; you don't have to be a genius[2] to design or to develop even a complex system or computer program using structured systems design techniques. As a matter of fact, beginners often find that this teaching approach removes much of the mystery from developing computer programs or systems. Our experience has been that nonprogrammers learn structured systems design very quickly and naturally, and are programming well within an amazingly short time — in many cases, as well as experienced analysts or programmers![3]

Even if you never again have reason to deal with a computer (which is unlikely), learning the methodology contained herein still should be valuable as an intellectual tool. After all, what can be better than learning how to think more productively? I have used the methodology and techniques of structured systems design to attack a variety of problems, many of which

---

[2]Indeed, if genius were really a prerequisite, there would be few of us left in the business.

[3]If an experienced programmer, you should take note, for you may have to adopt structured systems design in self-defense.

were totally outside the realm of computer systems, such as developing reports, plans, and organization charts. I can vouch for its usefulness and effectiveness in developing workable solutions.

Before Newton's time, engineering as a professional body of knowledge consisted largely of rules of thumb. The ancient engineer, only through long years of experience and apprenticeship, learned a great many things that would work in specific instances. Possessed of such knowledge and blessed with a great span of time, he was often able to do remarkable things: Witness the Gothic cathedrals. Unfortunately, confronted with an unusual or new circumstance, the ancient engineer modified an old approach to fit the problem — a risky situation, for he could not forecast the outcome of his new designs. [4]

As with any radical new approach, Newton's ideas were not fully accepted for decades after their publication; but the eventual changes in engineering and all the sciences that depended upon physics and mathematics were profound. With Newtonian mechanics, for example, engineers could predict with a high degree of certainty what would happen before they attempted to build something, even if it had never been tried before.

Systems technology currently is at a point strikingly similar to engineering's status soon after Newton began to publish his great discoveries. By our rules of thumb, we know some things have succeeded in the past, and others have failed. In some cases, we even have a vague idea of why they worked or failed. But with the knowledge gained in recent years, we now have a means to predict the success or failure of systems before we try them! Our present task is to put this new knowledge into practice.

Some of the fundamental ideas in this book originally were developed by Edsger Dijkstra in Holland and popularized in America by Harlan Mills, Terry Baker, and others. The ideas

---

[4]We know of the ancient engineers' successes, but time mercifully has erased most of their failures.

concerning the relationship of programs and data were most influenced by J.D. Warnier, whose works, unfortunately, have been available only in French until recently. To a lesser degree, some of the ideas presented here regarding programs and data are based on material passed along secondhand from Michael Jackson, based on discussions with students in his Association for Computer Machinery workshop on Advanced Programming.

If this book is unique in any way, it is so by virtue of my desire to synthesize and to communicate clearly this remarkable new technology to as wide an audience as possible. Those attempting to teach structured systems development face a severe handicap with the lack of good English texts aimed at the systems designer, programmer, and student. This book, I hope, will help overcome that problem.

I am indebted to scores of friends and students who have commented on and criticized my ideas and endured my enthusiasm. In particular, I would like to thank Ed Schmiedler, Bill Bryant, Pete Neely, Homer Sykes, and Bruce Taylor. I would also like to thank those who have typed and retyped these ideas over the years: Debbie Hassur, Debra Schell, and Karla Meggison. I would also like to thank some people whose support of my ideas gave me the opportunity to write this book at all: Bobby Langston and Pete Kitch. Finally, I would like to thank my wife, Marlene, for her professional editing and her nonprofessional support.

K.T.O.

Topeka, Kan.
September 1977

STRUCTURED SYSTEMS DEVELOPMENT

1

SYSTEMS ANALYSIS AND PROBLEM SOLVING

A great deal has been written about information systems and their uses. Despite this wealth of data, there is very little good literature on how to put a system together. The existing systems literature is largely concerned with some tool or other that can be used to simplify the process of building a system or with some foolproof method of documenting a systems job to speed up systems development and thereby reduce maintenance costs.

Clearly, systems building is still an art, and it is unlikely that this situation will change very much until we develop new methods for training systems designers and architects in the building of complex systems. This book is aimed at doing just that: teaching systems professionals new tools and approaches for analyzing, designing, developing, and installing those things we call systems. Many of the approaches and philosophies discussed in this book are refinements of techniques that have been around for decades, but others, especially the portion that has to do with structured systems design, are quite new. Taken together, they represent a body of knowledge that can be extremely useful. Although there is a quantity of material about programming and systems and their development, not a lot has been written from the standpoint of the person who does not receive a well-defined problem to solve.

Systems analysis and systems development are simply other terms to describe the process of problem solving. One great benefit of structured systems design is that it provides a number of significant new theories and tools for solving problems, especially complex, logical problems. By any definition, and in any disguise, problem solving is a heuristic process — a process of trial and error. Anyone who fails to recognize this is doomed from the outset either to outright failure or, at the very least, extreme frustration.

Most standard books on systems development describe what constitutes a good systems design. But there is a great deal of difference between a systems design and the process by which that systems design was actually conceived — i.e., between "the design" and "designing." Moreover, there is usually a great deal of difference between the system that was designed and the system that was actually built. Everyone is familiar with design flops, but isolating what went wrong is a very difficult task. One of the principal findings of structured systems design is that if one can develop a common set of tools for describing a problem from beginning to end, from user requirements through program design, then there is often a dramatic increase in understanding the system and its objectives — and an attendant decrease in problems.

Now is an excellent time to be learning these new techniques. For one thing, the process of systems building has become so complex that without some improved methods for systems analysis and development, the average systems analyst or programmer is faced with a nearly superhuman task. Twenty years ago, the systems analyst had only a meager set of tools and equipment at his disposal. Since that time, we have made dramatic breakthroughs in both hardware and software development. But many of them have been attained at very high costs, one of which being systems that are increasingly complex as well as expensive.

Another of the prices we have had to pay has been the increasing distance between the user's problem and its solution. In the early days of computing, the user, the analyst, and the programmer were often the same individual. But today, in most organizations, the natural tendency toward specialization has created situations in which a great many different individuals and groups are involved in the solution of a single problem, including analysts, programmers, teleprocessing specialists, data base specialists, and operating systems specialists, just to name a few.

In the movement from simple, small systems that were largely the product of one person to complex, large-scale systems that may be the product of hundreds of analysts and programmers, many new difficulties have arisen. For one thing, systems have become more expensive. For another, the time to install these systems has increased, often beyond the point of organizational endurance. Finally, the process has frequently gotten out of hand from the point of view of management.

Data processing is not alone. One of the natural tendencies of any new industry or profession is to develop a new tool or piece of equipment specifically whenever a new problem is encountered. While the early analyst and programmer were often limited by the tools and equipment at their disposal, at least they understood their tools. The machines on which they worked had only a limited number of simple instructions. That situation is anything but true today. In fact, many people suspect that a principal difficulty currently facing the typical systems analyst or programmer is that he has too many alternative methods to solve each problem and, in many cases, can't even figure out how to get started. Moreover, since the analyst hasn't actually used many of these methods, he is usually unsure of exactly what is possible. Unfortunately, the analyst knows enough to make a sound technical decision only after he finds that he has gotten himself into trouble.

Today, we must recognize that *we simply don't know how to teach someone to design a system very well.* While we can teach the various features of a programming language or of a data base management system, we have tremendous difficulties teaching someone how to put it all together. That is what systems development is all about — putting together all the pieces: the user requirements, the technology, and the management.

Where do we start? First, we have to recognize that although many people know how to design a system, for the most part they don't know how to tell anyone else how to do it.

That problem is not unique to systems analysis; most young professions have the same problem. This is particularly true when there is no strong underlying theory to guide the professionals in their field. This same situation existed in programming for many years; only with the advent of such concepts as structured programming and top-down development has it become possible to put programming on a more professional basis. We must now begin to do the same for systems analysis and design.

In the course of this book, I am going to try to show you how to understand what the requirements for a system are, and how to translate those requirements into an operational system. Although much of the discussion is directly applicable to computer systems, the approach is by no means limited to computer systems nor is it even computer-oriented. The secret to effective systems development of any kind, manual or automated, is clear logical thinking and expression — everything else is secondary. This last point is so important that I will stress it over and over: *Structured systems design is a method of logical analysis, design, and development; it can be used on any kind of system with any kind of language, computerized or not.*

What do you mean, "structured"?

> **Structure** *n* **1** : The action of building **2** : Something constructed **2a** : Something made up of interdependent parts in a definite pattern **3** : Manner of construction **4** : Arrangement of particles or parts in a substance or body **4a** : Interrelation of parts as dominated by the general character of the whole.
>
> **To structure** *vt* **1** : To form into a structure; organize **2** : Build, construct.
>
> — Webster's Unabridged Dictionary

Everything has a characteristic structure, and nearly everything we do involves structuring something or other. So to speak noisily about structured programming or structured systems design might suggest to some that there is an approach to programming or systems design that is not structured (nonstructured). Literally that isn't true, for all systems and all programming work is involved in structuring something. So the first time someone outside the data processing field encounters the term "structured" used in its current narrow technical sense, he is apt to be a little confused.

Unfortunately, as often happens, a common word — in this case, structured — has been given a specific technical definition that is not standard. Whenever this happens there is ordinarily a period of semantical confusion. During such a period, we hear conversations in which one group means one thing when using a word, and the rest of the world understands something else altogether. Edsger Dijkstra, who is credited with the formulation of structured programming, seems to have been the first to use structured to describe a specific approach to programming that has been expanded and applied to systems design. In recent years, as the term structured has come to be used somewhat indiscriminately, Dijkstra himself has become increasingly concerned that people not misinterpret what structured really means. In a sense, we become prisoners of our own words, and this is particularly apt to be the case with the word structured. Today we see discussions of structured walkthroughs, structured design, and structured analysis — who knows, perhaps tomorrow we'll see "structured coffee breaks" or "structured exit interviews."

In our terms, something is structured if and only if (1) it is hierarchically organized and (2) the pieces of each function are related to one another either by sequence, alternation, or repetition — the basic forms of logic. All structured things then are neatly hierarchical. For example, Figure 1.1b below is structured in our sense, while 1.1a is not.

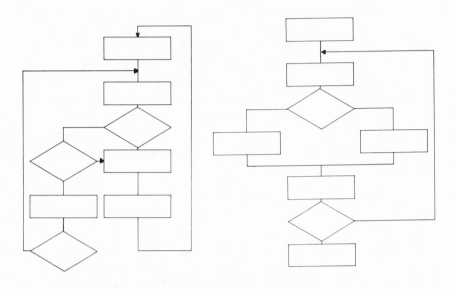

Figure 1.1a. Nonstructured chart.   Figure 1.1b. Structured example.

How about the following diagram? Is it structured or not?

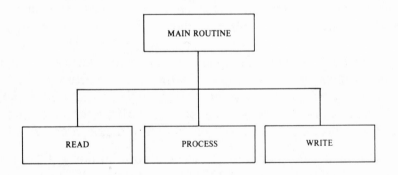

Figure 1.2. Hierarchical diagram.

It is hierarchical, certainly, but we can't tell if it's structured. In fact, the diagram above may be represented by either of the following, one of which is structured and the other is not:

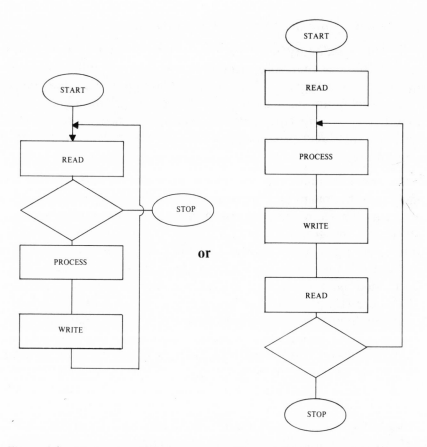

Figure 1.3a. Unstructured diagram.   Figure 1.3b. Structured diagram.

One way to tell if something is truly structured is to see if you can draw a box around any subset of the logic without crossing any lines. Truly structured things exhibit what mathematicians call a clean topology. However, the fact that structuring makes it possible to draw neater flowcharts would hardly have gotten anybody, except perhaps an occasional mathematician, excited if we hadn't come to recognize that anything that is clearly structured is logically structured as well.

Since all structured problem descriptions are neatly hierarchical, we can use a number of alternative means to describe our solutions. And if ever needed, we can switch effortlessly to another form to express our ideas.

One cautionary note — not everything that is hierarchical and modular is therefore structured. In fact, modular programming generally leads to much different solutions than does structured programming. Since structured programming is both modular and hierarchical, there recently has been a revived interest in modular programming, which has been around for a long time.

For example, the increased popularity of the *structured design* methodology of Constantine and Yourdon[1] (as opposed to structured systems design) is in part a result of the fact that structured programming naturally leads to breaking problems into well-organized modules. And since *structured design* is derived from an empirical study of the common characteristics of good modular programs, it provides a natural marriage. Moreover, there is a great deal to be gained from studying modularity. Since all good programs tend to look alike, what is learned in one area is often applicable in others. In fact, the use of the Constantine-Yourdon transform analysis often leads to program structures and systems very similar to those developed by our form of logical data structuring. While the Constantine-Yourdon form of structured design is not logically "structured" in the strict sense we use throughout this book, it does insist upon a definite systematically developed hierarchical structure, which is a major improvement over top-down, hierarchical design approaches.

Role of the systems analyst

Occasionally, people express surprise when they discover that structuring a system is mostly concerned with a different way of thinking about problems, and is not simply another programming trick. As it happens, most profound discoveries in science and the arts are simply new ways of looking at old problems; but since radically different outlooks require radical

---

[1]L. Constantine and E. Yourdon. *Structured Design* (New York: YOURDON inc., 1975).

psychological changes, it is often difficult to get people started. Because we are attempting to change the way you look at certain problems, we have had to adapt a set of entirely new tools to help show what we mean. Along with this, we have developed a number of examples to help you understand our points.

Probably as much as anything, the good systems analyst is characterized by the ability to understand what the systems' users in an organization are doing, visualize what they ought to be doing, and then develop systems to do what needs to be done. In other words, *the good systems analyst must be able to ask not only what, but why. And he must be able to do all this in a civilized manner.* In general, the systems analyst must be able not only to solve problems, but also to identify first what the problems are for himself. But this activity of sorting out the real problems is often overlooked.

Suppose we start where the systems analyst begins. Usually, he is faced with some major problems after first receiving an assignment to develop a new system. From the first day, there is often a basic misunderstanding about what is required. In case after case, I have seen projects in which enormous amounts of work had been done without any clear understanding of the goals or objectives.

To attack this problem, we have developed a simple approach to aid the analyst, or anyone else for that matter: That approach involves asking, How would I recognize a successful product (system) if somebody shipped it to me tomorrow? This technique is the outgrowth of structured systems designs' "output orientation." Looking for something measurable helps significantly in putting systems problems in perspective. The sad thing is that so many people start without that clear, measurable understanding of their goal.

The inability to set clear, measurable goals would be funny if it weren't so common. Human beings seem to want to do anything *other* than think through the problem. This unfortunate tendency means starting on details before the important work of setting goals and objectives has been completed. And getting started too early on the wrong thing leads in turn to a variety of dead ends. We will discuss some of these dead ends, but without a doubt the single largest cause of systems failures is not defining clear, understandable, and measurable goals at the outset.

The question, How would I know if I got there? is a central one for clearing the air. Why? Well, for one thing, if you, your boss, and the user can all agree early on how to tell whether you have succeeded when you're done, then you have eliminated a large potential for major misunderstandings.

Consider the following situation:

Jack Schnell, the manager of systems for Allied Arch Supports, has been asked by a user, Frank Swell, who heads Accounts Receivable, to look into a systems problem for him. At this time, all of Jack's experienced systems analysts are tied up, but Jack has a senior programmer, Ted Smart, who is available and who has shown some aptitude for systems analysis. Although Ted has had very little experience dealing with users or with accounting, he is a super programmer. Unfortunately in this case, Ted sees his job to be simply one of developing a computer system for Accounts Receivable. As the project proceeds, it becomes increasingly clear that Frank, although a very progressive manager, has no intention of computerizing the Accounts Receivable department at this time. Finally, after three months of systems work (including some programming), Ted reports to Jack, "They just don't want to use the computer!"

Was Ted right? Possibly. There certainly are people who require help but simply won't do what is required to overcome their problems. On the other hand, Ted started by assuming (wrongly) that the solution to every problem is a computer solution. This is particularly unfortunate, because many systems problems are to be found in the manual operation and in the people who operate them. Moreover, in this instance, Jack Schnell was wrong in letting Ted go as far as he did. All of these problems could have been avoided if Ted had been trained as a systems analyst. If each of the parties had come to an agreement at the outset about what they expected from the project, the failure to communicate would not have occurred. If, on the first day or in the first week of the project, the participants had asked themselves, How would we know if we finished successfully? they would have been way ahead. In this particular case, if Frank Swell had only said, "Well, I would be satisfied if you could help me lick our problems with the backlog of customer inquiries," Ted probably would have said, "You mean you want a computer system to do inquiries?" Then the stage would have been set for a dialogue about the real goals of the study and how to measure them. Frank would probably have made it clear that he was looking for a systems solution, not a computer solution. Even if they couldn't agree, Ted wouldn't have wasted his time and his company's money working on something that wasn't wanted.

Certainly, there's nothing new about the benefits of knowing your purpose. Obviously that's just good common sense. Surprisingly, however, in this age of technology and specialization, technicians many times will act like they have a solution to a nonexistent problem. This attitude, of course, is often encouraged by hardware and software vendors. In too many cases, a widening gulf develops between the man with the problem and the man charged with solving that problem.

Many of the most significant problems with systems work are related to simple, fundamental, and early misunderstandings about what should happen, and who is responsible for making those things happen. I suspect that most important bad decisions are made early. Surely, improving this early communication will likely increase the chances for the success of the entire project.

For the most part, systems analysts are recruited from the ranks of programmers. That's fine, but we should recognize that the two jobs often require different skills and that in many cases someone good at implementing part of a well-designed system may have difficulties in analyzing and designing a complete system for himself. In some cases, training as a programmer may even be counterproductive, because programmers who are only expected to program often learn to expect someone else to work out all the user problems beforehand. Upon becoming systems analysts, they often act as if the user should be able to express his systems requirements as well as an experienced systems analyst.

In fact, the user is rarely capable of expressing his desires clearly, and the analyst must be capable of helping the user express his needs. The analyst must be able to act as consultant, researcher, and adviser. Moreover, he must himself know how to set measurable goals, even when his client doesn't. He must continually ask himself how to know satisfactory completion. In other words, *the analyst must concentrate on the outputs of the systems process.*

How can structuring aid the systems process? There are a number of ways. The first and most familiar is to improve documentation of our existing systems, or to document the systems requirements with much more clarity and completeness than has been possible in the past. Because of the simplicity of such tools as Warnier Diagrams, users feel more comfortable in discussing complex systems requirements. They also feel that for the first time they can begin to understand what the data processing analyst proposes. Taking the mystery out of data processing is a major plus.

2 THE MODEL

In structured systems design, we take advantage of a number of tools and concepts that have been developed specifically to aid us in thinking about information handling. Most of these tools are simple to understand, but they are not always simple to use, at least not initially. As you come to understand the underlying theory, you will find their application more and more natural.

Structured systems design is an approach founded upon a rather simple systems model. That model is predicated on the fact that any (information) system can be considered of as consisting of three basic parts: (1) *output,* (2) a *black box* that produces the output, and (3) *input* from which the black box produces the output. (This might seem to be a peculiar way of saying that a system is made up of inputs, a black box, and outputs; however, you will see the point later.) A graphic version of the concept is shown below.

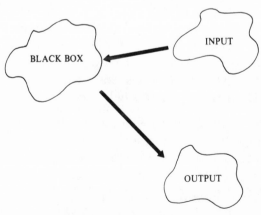

Figure 2.1. Structured systems design
based upon a three-part model.

In developing a system, the systems analyst needs a mental model. This one has certain advantages: (1) It's simple, (2) it's as clear as many of the systems you're apt to encounter in the real world, and (3) it leads to bigger and better things. But before talking about those bigger and better things, we need to refine our model a bit.

Suppose we begin by listing the things we know we ought to have, or have been told that we need, in a system. First, we will need outputs, since they are the principal reason to develop any system; and to produce outputs, we probably will need inputs. But what exactly do we mean by outputs and inputs? Do we mean, for example, reports or files, or pieces of paper, or bits coming over a telephone line? In general, by outputs we mean only those things with which the client of the system actually deals. For example, an output may be a report, a screen on a video terminal, or an audio response over a telephone. An input may mean a transaction form, a turnaround check, or a voice on a telephone. But in general neither term means electronic bits on a piece of tape or disk or an internal audit report. (These items are important, but they represent internal data — more about them later.)

In structured systems design, output and input (along with certain aspects of the black box) fall into a category called *systems requirements*. While dealing with a number of elements, *systems requirements are primarily concerned with outputs and the logical rules for their derivation*. Somewhat surprisingly, from a requirements standpoint, we are far less concerned with inputs than with outputs. The reasons for this will become more clear later.

If a change is made to a system and if it affects the output, then it is a change to the systems requirements. If, on the other hand, you convert a system from one computer operating system to another, or change the sequence of operations without affecting the output produced by the system, then that change is involved with the *systems architecture*. Systems architecture is involved with the way output is produced from input. While systems requirements primarily involve output and its derivation, systems architecture largely concerns the makeup of the black box, that is, the organization of the pieces of the system. Information is entered, processed, stored, and put out. Systems architecture is concerned with how this process will produce the correct results.

When we begin to develop a system (based on our past experience), we face some serious problems of understanding what we are to construct. Each of us carries in our head a model of what we're going to produce; and, indeed, if we didn't, we would never get anything accomplished. However, if your model is wrong, or if it leads you to do the wrong kinds of things, that mental model may make an already difficult job impossible. Our model, then, is based on the observations that the single most important feature of a system is its output, and that the easiest way to determine a system's effectiveness is if it always produces the desired output correctly. If it doesn't, you haven't succeeded in building a correct system, no matter how fast it runs, or what input it accepts.

Let's look at a system from another slightly different standpoint. Outputs and inputs can be thought of as "sets of data." For example, a payroll report can be considered a set of data about employees. Now, the black box in our model contains sets of data; but it also contains something else: "sets of actions" (or operations). *A correct system, then, is one in which the right sets of actions are executed on the right sets of data at the right times.* If the correct set of monthly actions (called report programs) are done on the right sets of data (called payroll files) at the right time (called accounting month end), then you will produce the right output and have a correct system. *A correct system is the minimum criterion for doing systems work.* In addition to producing the right output, though, you typically will also have to produce that output at a certain cost and within a given time frame prescribed by management. But first, you must produce the right answers.

But what are the right answers? Well, identifying them is half the systems analyst's job. That's why in our original model the outlines for the output, the black box, and the input were so fuzzy. In many cases, we simply don't know at the outset what the right answer is. A manager may know that he or she needs to have more timely information or needs to keep track of inventory, but not much in the way of detail. This doesn't mean that you will never convince a client to be specific about what he wants. In fact, many clients can be quite specific. But, you must understand that in most cases you will have to help the client think through his problem and come up with a system that helps him do a better job.

In general, my work with clients in developing a system has been a process of continuous refinement (and redefinition) of the problem to produce a solution. Many times, what the user says is the problem turns out to be only a symptom. Like a good doctor, a good systems analyst makes a point of looking beyond the symptoms to treat the underlying disease.

Usually in the first stages of the systems project, only a few fundamental systems requirements are absolutely certain, unless of course you've done exactly the same system before, and even then you have to be careful. In a payroll system, for example (see Figure 2.2), we know that we must produce pay checks and certain reports for the government.

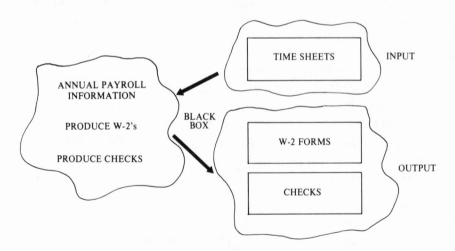

Figure 2.2. Fundamental systems requirements.

As we learn more about what we're attempting to systematize, we will find more reports that are mandatory, e.g., reports for local and state governments or basic accounting reports required by the accounting department or the firm's C.P.A. While there may be many such requirements, they are perhaps the easiest part of a system with which to deal, because they are usually well defined: The user knows what they must contain and how they must look. At this stage our system is beginning to take shape.

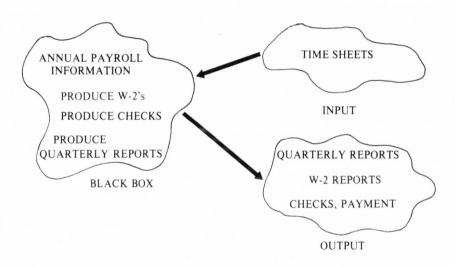

Figure 2.3. Additional systems requirements.

At each stage of refinement, we learn more about the system's sets of data and sets of actions. Intellectually, to deal with all this data, the analyst has to summarize or classify this in-mation into structures that can be manipulated easily. For example, the analyst might begin to talk about weekly reports or monthly reports as a group. Or he may categorize them into mandatory and optional, or federal and company. Each method of grouping may be useful, because it helps the analyst deal with the complexity of thousands of details. In fact, without some way of organizing information to find the big picture, it's highly unlikely that you'll ever get started. Many systems efforts fail simply because the analyst drowns in a sea of details. We must strive to avoid this pitfall. Again, our model can help. We said earlier that the black box part of our system can be considered as either sets of actions or sets of data. Let's show that graphically.

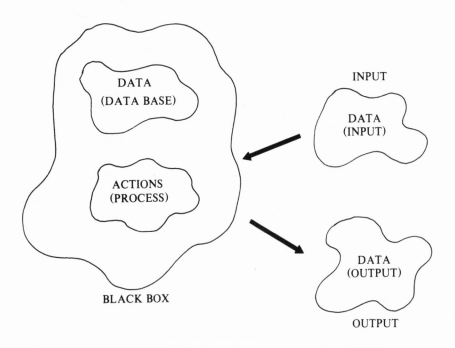

Figure 2.4. Black box part considered as sets of data or sets of actions.

This refinement of our systems model has added additional structure, for it shows how the basic pieces actually relate to one another. Now, we can think of a system in terms of the relation between sets of actions and sets of data. We also can give names to the major elements: output, process, data base, and input.

Conceptually, our model seems to fit our ideas of the real world. First, we collect information (input); then we process that information (process); we put out some of the processed information in the form of reports (output); and some of it we store for future use (data base). But we have to be careful because the most natural way of thinking about a problem involves input, process, output. Certainly, that's the way we're apt to process the data when the system is actually built, but it's not the order in which we consider things when we design a system!

To design a system, start with the output and work backward through the system until you finally arrive at the processing steps that are required, the data base that you need, and finally the inputs you have to collect. (At first glance, working backward in systems design seems unnatural. The reason is simply that starting at the beginning, i.e., with the inputs, and going forward doesn't work very well. It's a great deal like going on a trip without first having decided where you're going. How do you know what to pack? Since you don't know where you're going, you don't know what the weather will be, and, therefore, you'll probably take too much clothing, just in case. Your next problem is encountered the moment you leave the driveway. Which way do you go?)

The importance of having goals or objectives is clear in everything we do. But why, if everybody pays lip service to planning, goals, and so forth, do we so often botch our systems work? One reason is because we are simply not properly and sufficiently output-oriented. Later, we will see that starting at the input instead of at the output is often why we fail to complete many systems efforts successfully. Designing systems from the input is much like painting yourself into a corner. Think about it: To be at the right place when finished painting a floor (i.e., at the door), you have to work backward from the door to figure out where you should be to start. There's nothing very complicated about this approach, but it's harder to apply to systems design than you might think.

A number of benefits result from working backward. One major benefit is that in the ideal case (which will probably never happen), you won't collect or store data that you don't use — a factor certain to have a major effect on both the cost and the complexity of the end product, not to mention on questions of data security and privacy. Other benefits will be discussed as we uncover them.

Structured systems design aims at producing minimal systems. In this age of flexible, general, powerful systems, we want to design something that is minimal. What makes up a minimal system? How do you define it? *A minimal system does the absolute minimum to produce the desired outputs.* Such a system only captures data that appear as output or that affect something that comes out. Another way to look at our definition is to think of yourself as a mathematician who has derived a perfect formula for producing a correct systems design every time. In such a mathematical formula, if given a set of values for the independent variables, then all the dependent variables can be mechanically computed. But what exactly are the independent variables in systems design? They would be those elements that determine everything else, wouldn't they? What category of things that we deal with in systems work fits that description? The output, of course! If we change the output requirements, everything else in the systems design has to change to accommodate it. If the output changes minimally, we must change the processing; and if we don't have the data from which the new output is derived, then the change will affect the data base and the input as well. Therefore, *the output requirements can be thought of as independent variables of the systems process.*

Our model has four fundamental parts, some of which are more important than others. In general, we will want to concentrate on outputs and then work our way backward to determine what process, what data base, and what inputs will be needed to produce those outputs. So far, so good. We have a model, and we know at which end of the problem to start.

In theory, working backward from the output seems reasonable; and the more you think about it, the more you will realize that it's the *only* reasonable approach. In practice, however, working backward is difficult to apply. One of the major reasons is that thinking about outputs is hard work. It requires that you set up goals and objectives and that you make hard decisions such as, Why do I need this information? How do I want my information ordered? On the other hand, talking about input is much easier, for the hard questions always can be left until later; you don't have to be too specific about how you will use the information — you can simply say, We ought to collect it, because someday it may be needed. Most approaches in the past have indicated that one of the first systems tasks (right after specifying the outputs) is to define the inputs with the user. There are a number of strong pressures to consider the definition of input out of sequence.

In the next chapter, we will discuss the concepts of analysis and synthesis as tools in the process of systems building; and after describing some of the tools that can be used in structured systems design, we will then return to our model of a system and begin to see how to apply what we already know to systems building.

So far, we've talked mostly in generalities, but we're laying the groundwork for other things. In particular, we're attempting to help you, the analyst, see how a system grows from the idea stage to a tangible operation. Design is tough but fun work; however, it can easily get out of hand. Too often, we promote people into responsibilities of systems analysis without teaching them how to do systems analysis or design. This can prove to be a major mistake. As with any activity, there are right ways to attack the designing and implementing of a system and there are wrong ways. We're learning that many of the old guidelines about systems building are really only myths. We've needed a new improved model for some time. Now that we have one, we're beginning to see the results of having a better model with which to work.

3 ANALYSIS, SYNTHESIS, AND PROCESS FLOW

·In the last chapter, we began to develop an intellectual model for an information system. We will return to that model after we have looked at how some traditional approaches to systems analysis and design are used. The purpose in introducing traditional approaches at this point is to give us practice in systems work before we must use our knowledge in a structured environment.

The model in the last chapter served a very important function: It gave us a conceptual framework or theory. We will pick up more theory as we proceed. Many of us go through our entire lives without recognizing the importance of theory in everything we do, primarily because theories seem too abstract and remote to be of much use. Often people in new professions are too busy *doing* to reflect much about *what* they are doing or *how* it relates to other things.

Take computer programming as an example. For years, people developed program after program, using a variety of machines and languages, convinced that programming was at best an art. Most programmers felt that while you could learn programming, there weren't any scientific ways of writing a correct program. A good program was simply a program that worked, and the only way to know whether a program actually worked was to test and test and test. Even then, you couldn't be absolutely sure it would always work. Today, we know there are better ways of developing correct programs. We know, for example, that if we understand logically what we want to do, we can build a correct program to do it. Moreover, we are quite certain that we can make our programs work, if not the first time, at least within a few tries. How has this transition from doubt to certainty in programming taken place in such a short time? The answer simply is that we now have a theory to guide our activities — a theory for programming. We now know that if we work out all the logical possibilities in detail and construct our program in a hierarchical logical fashion, it will work. We also know that we can use the structure of the data as a guide for the construction of our program, thereby eliminating many tough decisions once facing us in organizing or structuring our programs.

If we apply this same technique of hierarchical logical analysis to an entire system, we can become increasingly certain that we will develop a correct system, i.e., one that performs the right sets of actions on the right sets of data at the right times. There are a number of differences, however, between the design and construction of a program and the design and construction of an entire system. For one thing, the programmer ordinarily has fewer worries than has the systems analyst. Often an analyst or someone else already has defined the outputs and inputs and the basic processing for the programmer. So while the programmer has to figure out many details, he doesn't have to define basic parameters.

The analyst, on the other hand, is in a different situation: He not only has to figure out what needs to be done, he has to do it as well. *Nothing except the problem is given to the analyst.* He has to add his own ideas to the wishes of the various people who must interact with the system to define the scope of the problem. This becomes the *why* and *what* of the system. Then he has to figure out a way in which to do these things — the *how* and *when* of the system.

Working out this relationship is integral to the process of design. Clearly, the determination of why and what and of how and when are related. In a classical sense, we are talking about two activities: analysis and synthesis. Therefore, we will look at *systems analysis* and *systems synthesis* (also called design or integration) and see how they relate to the real process of designing a system.

> **analysis,** n (pl — **yses**). Resolution into simple elements.
>
> — Webster's Unabridged Dictionary

Analysis is an old word meaning to break something into its fundamental pieces. That definition is true whether referring to chemical analysis, linguistic analysis, or systems analysis. *In systems analysis, we are concerned with breaking a system into pieces and with the tools for doing that.* In general, there is a hierarchical approach characteristic of all types of analysis; that is, break something big into successively smaller pieces, until it is no longer possible to further subdivide any of the pieces. Each new piece is subordinate to the piece above.

How does the process of hierarchical analysis actually work? Let's take an example: Suppose you are assigned the problem of developing a system to produce a monthly statistical report, as represented below:

Figure 3.1. Problem to produce monthly report.

In hierarchical analysis we ask, How can we break this job into a series of simpler ones? One way is to think of some of the problem's basic parts that might expectedly meet the original problem definition. In this case, our goal is to develop a system that produces a monthly statistical report. From past experience, we might expect (at least on the computer side) to produce that monthly report in a number of steps: For example, one part of the system would produce the report, one part would update the master file (or data base) from which the reports will be produced, and one part would edit the input data initially to exclude any erroneous values. The typical method of showing the relation is to draw something resembling an organizational chart:

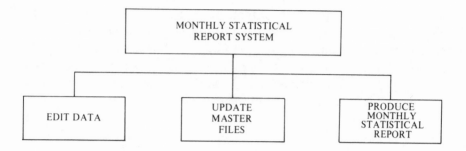

Figure 3.2. Hierarchical analysis requires problem breakdown.

A similar hierarchical analysis is conducted in nearly every systems job and, in fact, is so common and natural that many analysts don't even bother to write it down. They simply assume that everyone understands how they arrived at their design. This is often not the case and it is important for those who will implement, maintain, or operate a system also to understand how it was constructed.

The analysis of a problem into parts is a useful process, and it is most effective if you continue systematically to apply the same process of divide and conquer to each part of the problem. For example, we might subdivide (or analyze) the part called PRODUCE MONTHLY STATISTICAL REPORT into several parts: one to read the master file, one to summarize the data, and one to format and print the report as follows:

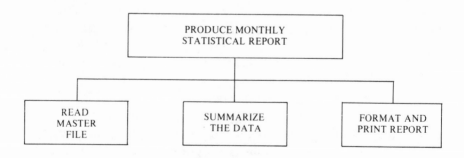

Figure 3.3. More detailed breakdown of problem into steps.

Indeed, we could do the same with all the other pieces of the puzzle:

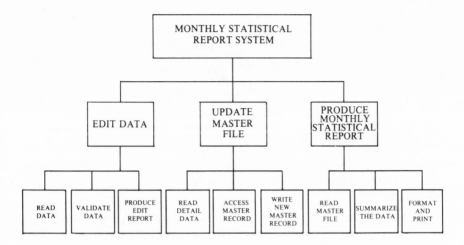

Figure 3.4. The process continues.

In a complete analysis, this process continues until each of the pieces is so simple that there is no need to break them down further. If carried on systematically, analysis is an extremely powerful tool. When finished, you will have a complete idea of what needs to be done, and how to do it.

Conceptually, analysis is a simple technique that should work all the time. Over the years, nearly every successful systems analyst has employed some form or other of hierarchical analysis. Currently, analysis is enjoying new popularity under the name of top-down design, which recommends that each problem be analyzed step-by-step until it is completely resolved. The HIPO (Hierarchical-Input-Process-Output) methodology utilizes hierarchical analysis quite extensively.

You might wonder why, if hierarchical analysis is so natural and so popular, we haven't used it more in the past. There are a number of reasons. One is that it seems like a lot of work, especially at the lower levels. Further, it requires that you have some idea of the top of the system and of the major pieces at each step. Finally, hierarchical analysis poses the question: How do we know what pieces to break the system into in the first place?

This problem is a tricky one. The example above of a monthly reporting system was uncomplicated, but suppose we had to build a total management information system? Certainly the problem would be more complex, and the analysis normally would be very difficult to do from the top down. For that reason, hierarchical analysis has not been recognized as a fundamental tool in systems work until only very recently despite its common use.

Analysis has an important by-product: making systems that are both hierarchical and modular. This is extremely important, for our experience suggests that all good systems are both hierarchical and modular. However, analysis does not deal easily with one fundamental design question: How are the pieces (modules) of the hierarchy related to one another? This question is a principal concern of synthesis.

If analysis is involved with breaking a problem into its pieces, then *synthesis is involved with putting the pieces of a system together.* In fact, a term often used to mean synthesis is "integration," for synthesis is concerned with order and with time. If analysis is concerned with why and what, then synthesis is concerned with how and when.

In design we see two phases: breaking down and fitting together. In our example, the system was broken into a number of parts: one that edited the transactions, one that updated the master file, and one that produced the monthly report. But we can arrange those pieces derived from the analysis stage in a number of different ways. For example, both of the systems in Figure 3.5 have the same pieces. The experienced systems analyst will recognize that Figure 3.5b is a more realistic solution than is 3.5a. Although the major pieces are the same, the questions of when and how have been considered in more detail.

Also, an additional piece has been discovered that we missed in our first analysis (or included in our definition of EDIT DATA). In fitting the pieces together again, we often find that we have omitted some basic consideration or included something extraneous. When this occurs, we have to repeat the process of analysis. In our example, if we decide to include a piece to FIND AND CORRECT ERRORS (and it seems unlikely that we wouldn't), we will have to analyze that statement into its appropriate pieces (see Figure 3.6).

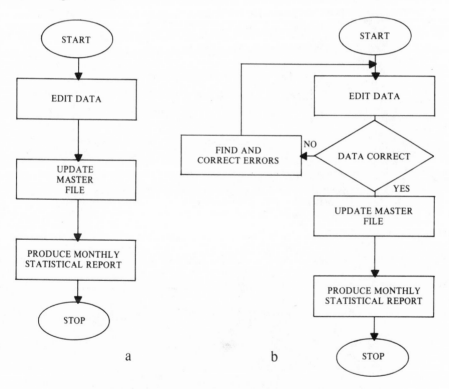

Figure 3.5. Comparing two systems (a,b) with identical parts.

Earlier, we mentioned briefly the difference between the design and the process of designing. Now, our words become clearer. On the one hand, after putting the pieces together again we have a finished design, or at least a better one than we had initially.

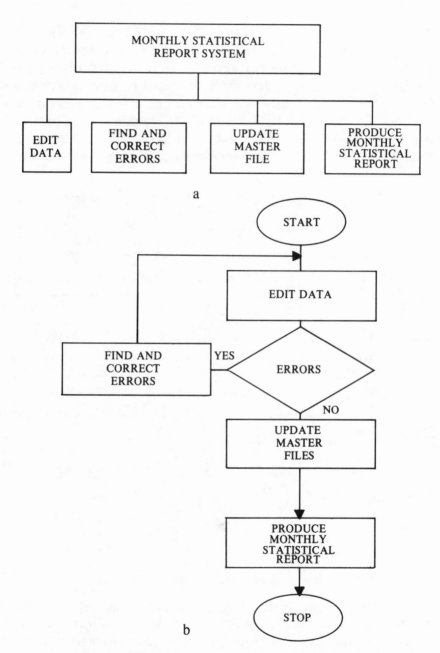

Figure 3.6. Structure chart with additional command (a)
and analysis of that piece (b).

Unless the reader of such a diagram has a copy of all the inter-mediate analysis steps and charts used to develop this design, he is apt to think that we came up with the final design the first time. Many times, beginning analysts are frustrated by the pro-cess of analyzing, integrating, analyzing, integrating, and so on. They feel they must be doing something wrong, because they look at other people's finished designs and assume that they didn't have to go through any periods of trial and error. These beginning analysts simply confuse the design with the process of designing. Making mistakes is no sin — failing to recognize and deal with them, however, can be fatal.

Recently, we have seen the process of analysis and integra-tion (or synthesis) combined in a single approach called top-down development. As distinguished from top-down design, top-down development requires not only that your problem be analyzed into pieces, but also that those pieces be built and test-ed together as a structure of the solution before any of the pieces can be analyzed in great detail. By forcing continuous integra-tion, top-down development seeks to avoid many of the more serious problems that have limited past use of hierarchical analysis.

Thus far in this section, we have tried purposely to avoid discussions of structuring the systems process or of using the model explained in the previous chapter. We wanted to concen-trate on the ways we design systems today, for structured sys-tems design has a great deal in common with traditional methods. The difference is largely in terms of emphasis and focus. Therefore, before introducing any formal structuring, I wanted the reader to understand the traditional concepts of analysis and synthesis as applied to systems building.

Traditionally, systems analysis and synthesis have been used in conjunction with yet another technique called "process flow." In looking at things from the process flow standpoint, we usually attempt to find out what happens when. To analyze a problem, we use current processing steps as a clue to tell us to break our problem into pieces. In synthesis or integration, we visualize what the process steps will have to be to make the whole thing work.

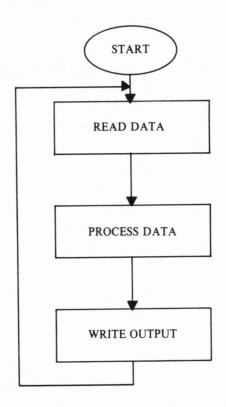

Figure 3.7. Basic programming model.

Programmers have used the process flow approach as the primary means of designing their programs. In fact, the systems or program flowchart is still the most common documentation tool in use anywhere. Figure 3.7 is perhaps the most common programming model expressed in terms of a simple flowchart.

Process flow is a natural and compelling design approach because you start at the beginning and proceed to the end. Unfortunately, it also has many shortcomings. One thing seems to lead to another, but proceeding from a general process flow diagram to a more detailed one may lead to design problems. For example, in the simple program given above, there is an infinite loop, or error, since the program fails to provide a means for stopping; i.e., it appears simply to ignore the signal that it is out of data. Making this model workable then requires the following modification:

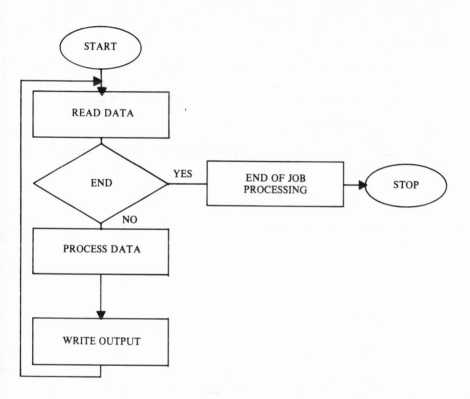

Figure 3.8. Corrected basic programming model.

It is unavoidably characteristic of process flow designs that as new logical conditions crop up (call them exceptions), the basic overall process flow becomes harder to recognize. As we learn more about program development, the less attractive we find process flow as a method of designing either a program or a system. Because process flow designs habitually become extremely complex, and since designing with process flow is fundamentally a trial-and-error method, we usually end up with far more error than is acceptable.

But no matter what our feelings are about process flow designs, any finished system must assure that the proper processes happen at the right times within a system. Fortunately, hierarchical structuring makes this possible in ways never suspected a few years ago. At the same time, it eliminates much of the confusion and complexity of earlier process flow systems designs.

We've now seen a few of the principal tools of traditional systems design: systems analysis, systems synthesis (or integration), and process flow. Let's put these elements together in a new way I referred to earlier as structured systems design. This method allows us to combine the tools of analysis, integration, and process flow in a logical fashion and, moreover, to take advantage of our basic model of a system.

4 STRUCTURED TOOLS – WARNIER DIAGRAMS

Some methods for doing systems work are more productive than others, and each method has advantages and disadvantages. We want tools that both maximize the advantages and minimize the disadvantages. As stated before, structured systems design techniques seem to meet those requirements better than anything else we've seen.

The first structured design tool is the *Warnier Diagram.* Warnier Diagrams are named for Jean-Dominique Warnier (pronounced Warn-yeh) who was the first person, to my knowledge, to systematically apply hierarchical logical methodology to building systems. A Warnier Diagram is fundamentally a series of brackets used with a small number of other symbols to portray a problem.

The best way to appreciate the power of Warnier Diagrams is to use them. Suppose we take the earlier problem and show how to employ these Warnier Diagrams to express the same thoughts, as follows:

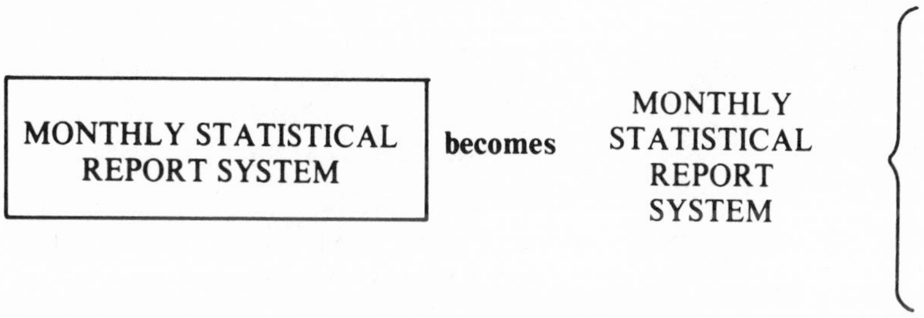

MONTHLY STATISTICAL REPORT SYSTEM	**becomes**	MONTHLY STATISTICAL REPORT SYSTEM {

Figure 4.1. Example of a Warnier Diagram.

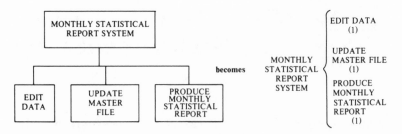

Figure 4.2. Warnier Diagram as a structured tool.

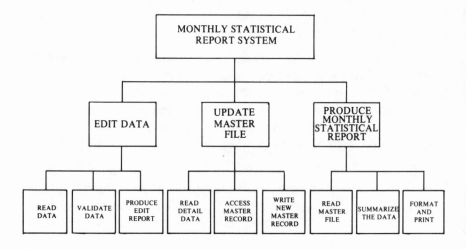

becomes

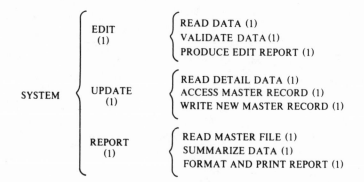

Figure 4.3. Using a Warnier Diagram.

A Warnier chart can be regarded simply as an organizational chart (or tree diagram) laid on its side. However, we can do things with Warnier Diagrams that are not possible with other hierarchical forms of organization — for example, dealing with logic, repetition, and sequencing.

Remember that in the first analysis of our simple reporting system, we had some problems; and, during the synthesis step, we had to add another piece (module) and some logic to the system. Warnier charts can be used to show this easily:

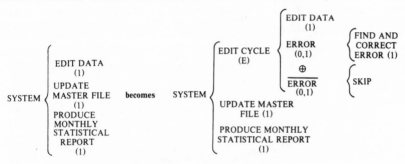

Figure 4.4. Warnier charts showing changes to the system.

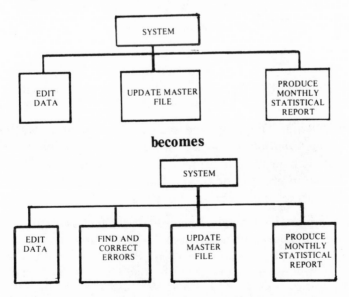

becomes

Figure 4.5. Hierarchical chart with additional module.

You will recall that the hierarchical organization chart we used failed to show the emerging relationship between the various modules (see Figure 4.5). The Warnier Diagram at left in Figure 4.4, on the other hand, was modified to contain all aspects of both process flow and hierarchical analysis. How did we do that? The symbols in the parentheses below the names of each piece in the diagram at the right represent the number of times that each piece occurs. Figure 4.6 illustrates this:

UPDATE MASTER FILE (1)	means	The module Update Master File is executed 1 time at this point.
EDIT CYCLE (E)	means	The module Edit Cycle is executed E times at this point, where E is a variable.
ERROR (0,1)	means	The module Error is executed 0 or 1 times depending upon whether there was an error.
̄ERROR ̄ (0,1)	means	The module Not Error is executed 0 or 1 times depending upon whether there was an error.
⎧ ERROR ⎪ (0,1) ⎨ ⊕ ⎪ ̄ERROR ̄ ⎩ (0,1)	mean	The modules Error and Not Error are mutually exclusive, and only one of them will be executed.

Figure 4.6. Explanation of process flow and hierarchical analysis
in a Warnier Diagram.

In Warnier Diagrams *the sequence of activity is presumed to be left to right and top to bottom.* So, a Warnier Diagram always is concerned with order and sequence, whereas a typical hierarchical organization chart is not. The following description is roughly what the Warnier chart above expresses:

> The system is defined as an edit cycle that is performed some variable number of times (until no more errors) followed by a set of actions to update the master file, followed by a set of actions to produce the monthly statistical report. The edit cycle is defined as a set of actions to edit the input or a mutually exclusive set of actions if there are no errors

in the input. If there are errors in the input, then a set of
actions to find and correct the errors is executed.

Later, we will see a mechanical method of converting a Warnier
Diagram into a process flow diagram, if required.

Now, you will have noticed that we have again returned to
talking about sets of actions. Indeed, in a Warnier Diagram, the
names of the pieces describe a set of actions, and the bracket to
the right of the name explains in detail how that piece (module)
is accomplished. Consider the example below:

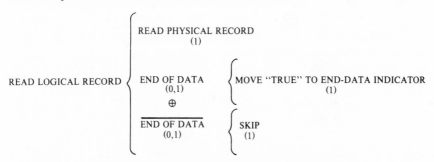

Figure 4.7. Example of a Warnier Diagram.

In this case, the pieces READ PHYSICAL RECORD and MOVE
"TRUE" TO END-DATA INDICATOR probably can be executed
directly and, therefore, do not require any additional definition.

Structured systems design ultimately involves developing a
hierarchical Warnier Diagram from the top for the entire system.
Unfortunately, the top of a Warnier Diagram is on the left side
and top-down implementation means left to right (a small problem in mental gymnastics that you will get used to).

When you've finished a structured systems design, you will
have broken your problem into sequences of things to do,
hierarchically organized, using only alternation, repetition, and
sequence as a means of structuring. This seems simple, and
especially compared to traditional methods, is simple. On the
other hand, it is not all that intuitively obvious, but, of course,
nothing worth having is ever that simple. Otherwise, people
would have discovered it a long time ago. Warnier Diagrams not
only allow us to break down problems hierarchically, logically,

and in a readily understandable graphic method, but they also present us with some new unexpected approaches. Let's see what those are.

When we initially employed analysis to break our system into pieces, we did so more or less arbitrarily. We chose three pieces — EDIT, UPDATE, and REPORT — because they seemed natural. At the next level, we broke each of the major pieces into another set of three pieces, characterized as READ, PROCESS, and WRITE. These forms of program structures are characteristic of most systems. But the very obviousness of these modules hides the fact that they are not necessarily the only or even the most logical means of constructing a program or a system.

Let's return to our model and see if it can help us. Discussing the model, we said that correct systems design was a process of working backward from the output to the input. Moreover, we said that correct systems design was involved in getting the right sets of actions performed on the right sets of data at the right times. How can we apply that model here? Suppose we put the information gained about our system into the model itself, as shown below.

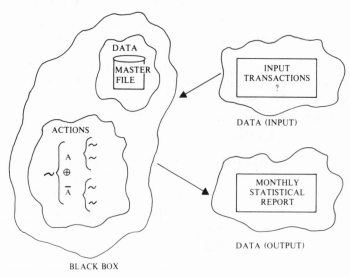

Figure 4.8. Revised model of our system.

We can see in the above figure that there is a place for all of the information accumulated about the system, but we would like to be more specific. We need a better means of showing this information while preserving our systems model, say, with a modified type of Warnier chart (these modifications, by the way, are not Warnier's but my own).

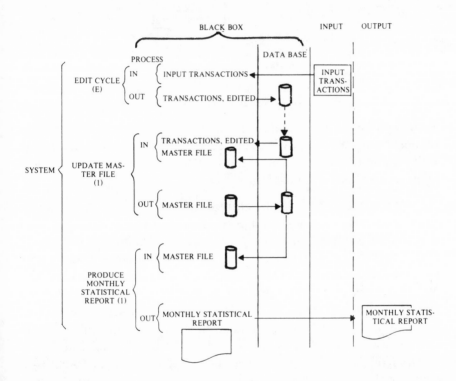

Figure 4.9. Modified Warnier chart.

That seems to work pretty well. In fact, if we only wanted to talk about systems requirements, leaving out consideration of systems architecture for the moment, we could do so very simply, just by eliminating everything within the system except for the major inputs and outputs, as shown on the next page:

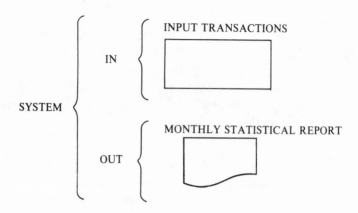

Figure 4.10. Systems requirements model.

So far, so good. Our model seems to be working out as a means of describing all the various aspects of our problem, simple as well as complex. Let's see now if it will help us to understand even more about the problem.

As stated before, a structured systems designer focuses initially on output and works backward from there. However, the method of systems analysis discussed in Chapter 3 didn't do that, did it? As a matter of fact, experience suggests that traditional techniques don't incorporate output-oriented thinking unless you concentrate on doing so. Since we have only one output in our example system, it is relatively simple to see what part of our system should be examined in detail — the monthly statistical report. But what questions do we ask? The traditional method of discussing output has been for the analyst to ask the user for his rough information needs (and his intended uses) and then to develop a detailed layout showing all the appropriate fields. Although eventually we also will want most of the same information, in a structured systems design we are interested initially in other things, particularly in knowing the logical structure of the report.

What do we mean by that? The logical structure is more or less the hierarchy, or sequence, of the report. When the user says, "I'd like to see customer sales data by salesman, by district, and by region," he's talking about the data structure of the report. If our monthly statistical report was designed precisely in that sequence, that would be the logical structure as follows:

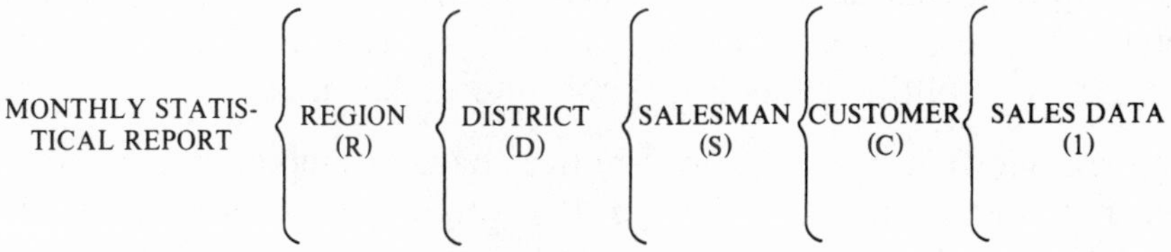

MONTHLY STATIS-
TICAL REPORT
REGION
(R)
DISTRICT
(D)
SALESMAN
(S)
CUSTOMER
(C)
SALES DATA
(1)

Figure 4.11. Report's logical structure.

Historically, the sequence of a report always has been considered significant in program design. Since the earliest days of data processing, input files to produce reports have been sorted into the same hierarchical sequences as the report to save space (and time) on machines, especially those with limited capacity. Before computers, we had accounting machines, and before that we had tabulating machines. These machines in conjunction with sorting machines solved complex problems using only a few primitive operations.

MONTHLY SALES STATISTICS
SALES REGION IDENTIFICATION
SALES DISTRICT IDENTIFICATION
SALESMAN IDENTIFICATION
Sales
Profit
CUSTOMER IDENTIFICATION
SALES AMOUNT
PROFIT AMOUNT
SALESMAN TOTAL
Σ CUSTOMER SALES AMOUNT
Σ CUSTOMER PROFIT AMOUNT
DISTRICT TOTAL
Σ SALESMAN SALES AMOUNT
Σ SALESMAN PROFIT AMOUNT
REGION TOTAL
Σ DISTRICT SALES AMOUNT
Σ DISTRICT PROFIT AMOUNT
COMPANY GRAND TOTAL
Σ REGION SALES
Σ REGION PROFIT

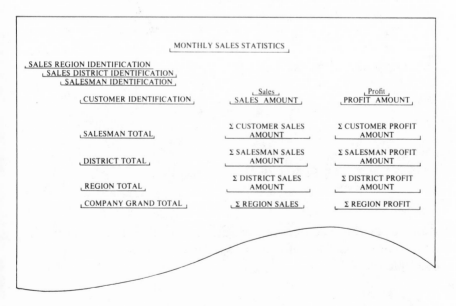

Figure 4.12. Report layout.

· The hierarchical structure of the sorted file made all this possible. Now, that same idea of hierarchically structured files is a natural means of organization using structured design. Having defined the structure of our report, we can be more specific about the monthly statistical report and its layout.

Following closely, you'll notice that we slipped in a number of new requirements between the original discussion and the final specification for the report. Where did this new information originate? As we talked to our hypothetical user, he thought of more and more things he would like to see in the report, a typical reaction. As he did so, however, the problem changed somewhat. He added a new field to the output, labeled PROFIT; and he introduced a COMPANY GRAND TOTAL to the report. These are natural expected modifications. In fact, don't be surprised if the user makes many additional changes before completion.

With the revised specifications, let's redo our Warnier Diagrams to reflect these changes.

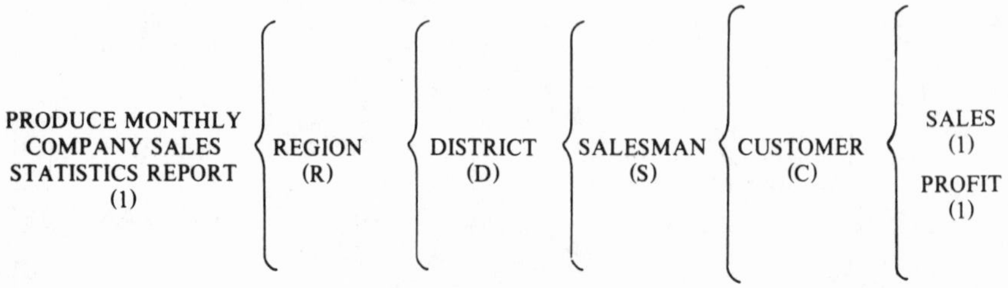

| PRODUCE MONTHLY COMPANY SALES STATISTICS REPORT (1) | { | REGION (R) | { | DISTRICT (D) | { | SALESMAN (S) | { | CUSTOMER (C) | { | SALES (1) PROFIT (1) |

Figure 4.13. Revised Warnier Diagram.

Remember that each bracket represents a set of actions and each level represents a set of actions within a set of actions. From our example, we can say:

For the company do the following:
     For each region within the company do the following:
          For each district within the region do the following:
               For each salesman within the district do the following:
                    For each customer of the salesman do the following:
                         Print customer sales and profit.

Roughly, we would be correct, but we need to be more specific than that with structured systems design. We'll come back to this report later. First, let's fit this new information into our old diagram.

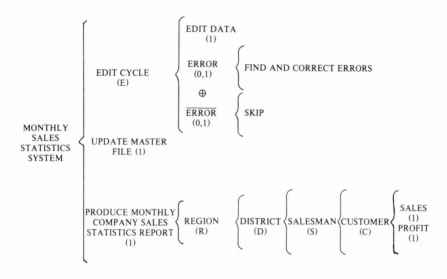

Figure 4.14. Warnier Diagram with additional output structure.

We didn't have any trouble working the output structure into our Warnier Diagram. But it is certainly different from the original model. Our new structure has a lot more resemblance to the problem than the original one, and that should prove helpful if the user later changes his mind regarding the desired output.

Returning to our original discussions about correctness, we said that correct systems design involves getting the right sets of actions done on the right sets of data at the right times. We've been largely concerned with the right sets of output data and with the right actions. Suppose we draw a Warnier Diagram of the structure of the data needed to produce a correct report:

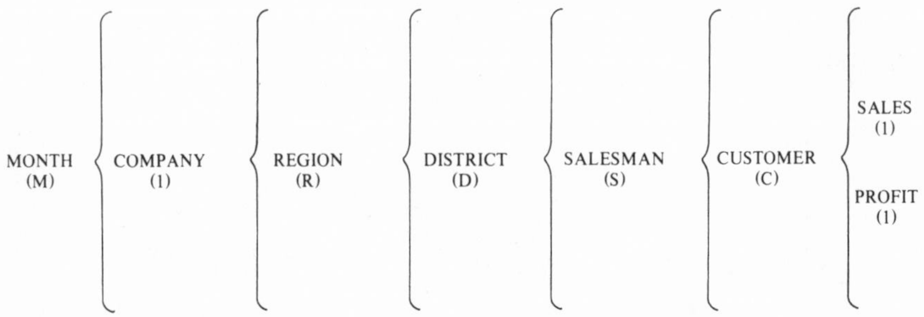

MONTH (M) { COMPANY (1) { REGION (R) { DISTRICT (D) { SALESMAN (S) { CUSTOMER (C) { SALES (1) / PROFIT (1)

Figure 4.15. Warnier Diagram of data structure.

Where did the MONTH level come from? We picked it up from the title (often things like the frequency or period of a report are omitted from the definition of requirements). But we don't have any monthly considerations in the Warnier Diagram of our system! Let's see if we can insert them in the diagram in Figure 4.16.

Our revised diagram now means we're going to do certain things over again every month. As a matter of fact, that change has made our system into a continuous operation rather than a one-time shot, something the users always wanted even if they couldn't say so. Many times, we must add a new level to the systems diagram after integrating some new information into the systems architecture. Adding this new level often solves many problems and the technique has been so common in our work that we have given it a name: "finding the hidden hierarchy."

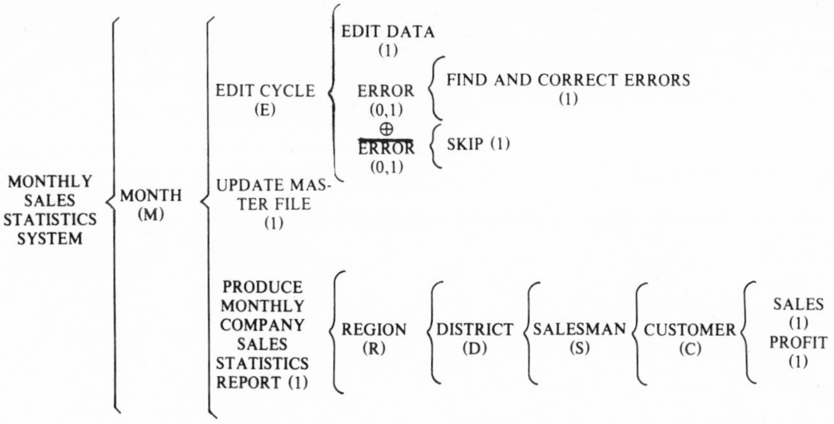

Figure 4.16. Warnier Diagram showing continuous system.

In the last two chapters, we've seen only the tip of the structured systems design iceberg. Using a number of traditional techniques for analyzing systems in traditional ways, we've come up with traditional systems designs. We've also begun to use some structured techniques such that our example system, after its usual start, now has begun to look increasingly structured. However, at this point, we shouldn't be at all surprised that our approach contains elements of both traditional and structured approaches. Many structured techniques have grown out of traditional ones, and traditional techniques are easy to grasp, accounting in part for their widespread use.

By introducing Warnier Diagrams and by applying some rules drawn from our model, we have been able to show both the hierarchical and the process flow (including logic) of our system. As we use these charts more in our work, we find that they are of tremendous value. Warnier charts are rapidly becoming the flowchart of the future, for they show a complete problem solution in an easy-to-grasp graphic form.

5 MORE ABOUT WARNIER DIAGRAMS

In the last chapter, we used Warnier Diagrams to portray the structure of a system. The development of structured systems becomes considerably easier if the user is proficient in the construction of these diagrams; therefore, this section explains in some detail the various forms of Warnier Diagrams.

Sets of actions

The Warnier Diagrams we've seen have been used primarily to describe sets of actions. By subdividing each piece into simpler pieces, and by providing a simple means for dealing with order and logic, the Warnier Diagram provides a major benefit over other structured documentation tools, such as HIPO charts or pseudocode. Other uses of a Warnier Diagram follow:

> Problem — We wish to obtain statistics from a file of employees of a university. If a staff member is part of the teaching faculty, then count him as such. If the staff member is part of the nonteaching faculty, count him as such. If he is not on the faculty, count him simply as nonfaculty.

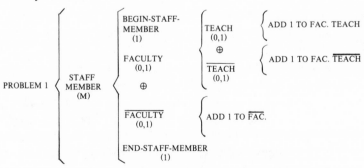

Figure 5.1. Warnier Diagram of problem statement.

In this case, our Warnier Diagram helps to express a systems problem simply, completely, and logically. It is, then, a relatively small matter to turn this problem statement into a problem solution. In fact, from one viewpoint, *in structured systems design the proper definition of the problem is the solution.*

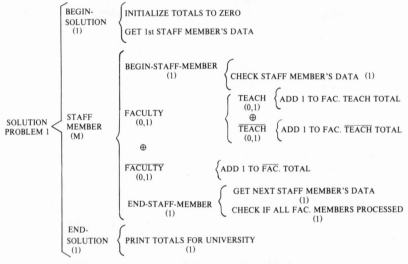

Figure 5.2. Warnier Diagram of problem solution.

Warnier Diagrams allow us to concentrate on the logical requirements of a problem instead of on the physical ones. This is particularly beneficial in dealing with users. Indeed, because users are normally put off by jargon and technical terms, the ability of stating problems in a fashion understandable to a user helps significantly to overcome many of the serious communications problems that always have kept us away from the problem. Structured systems design restricts us to the use of *operations* (or sets of actions), *sequence of operations, repetition of operations,* and *alternation* (or selection) between operations. Only a few years ago, most of us would have found this list of possible operations impossibly restrictive. Today, however, based on theoretical and practical experiences with structured programming and structured systems design, we know that these forms of representation are enough. Moreover, we now know that there is a fundamental relationship between these forms and logic, the foundation of all mathematics.

Sets of data

Warnier Diagrams are useful for describing not only logical sets of operations but logical sets of data as well. Suppose we had to describe the following data set:

A customer master file is composed of records. For each customer there is one customer header record containing customer number, record type, and customer name. This is followed by a variable number (possibly zero) of customer orders, which are followed by a variable number of customer accounts receivable transactions (possibly zero).

In the past, we would have shown this file schematically as follows:

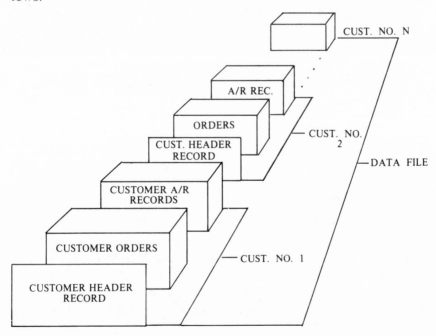

Figure 5.3. Data structure of customer master file.

For the most part, when thinking of data, we have thought of files as being made up of records, and records made up of fields. In fact, our experience with structured systems data base designs indicates that we're dealing with sets and subsets of data. The Warnier Diagram of the above data structure follows:

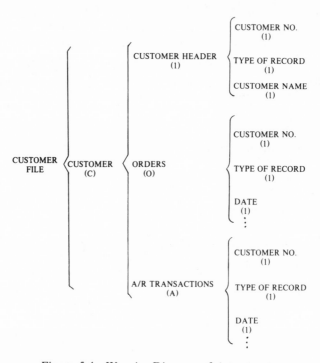

Figure 5.4. Warnier Diagram of data structure.

The use of Warnier Diagrams to describe, graphically, complex data structures is of particular value to a systems designer. As our problems have become more complex, their data structures often have grown more complex with them. This tends to lead to serious confusion. We need new methods of documenting exactly how data files are structured. Data base diagrams, pioneered by Bachman[1] and others, have helped to show that logical hierarchical organization chart methods are not as explicit

----

[1]C.W. Bachman, "Data Structure Diagrams," *Data Base,* Vol. 1, No. 2 (Summer 1969).

as Warnier Diagrams when describing all relevant logical facts. Take the following example:

> Problem — Describe a file that is made up of two types of customers: individuals and businesses. For individuals, only basic information and records of purchases are kept. For businesses, in addition to information about the firm, data is kept with respect to purchase's by each of its locations. Customers are either individuals or businesses.

The data base diagram for this problem only approximates the problem statement.

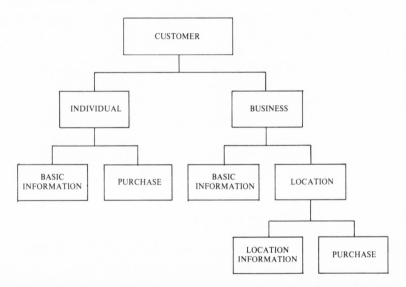

Figure 5.5. Data base diagram.

By contrast, the Warnier Diagram describing the same file (see Figure 5.6) follows the problem exactly. As we will see later, this exactness makes it possible to develop data structured programs to process structured data files.

The use of Warnier Diagrams to define data structures makes many things possible, not the least of which is improved maintenance of systems. In the past, people often have defined very complex data structures with the (expressed) aim of improving the efficiency of some aspect of their processing. But more often than not, as the people on the original design team moved to other presumably better jobs and as new people took their places, maintenance problems arose due to misunderstandings about the data structure. As a consequence, old programs were difficult to maintain and new programs difficult to debug. Invariably, since new people assigned to those systems took such a long time to understand how the system worked, a small number of unfortunates were eventually stuck with maintenance of the system — that is, until they quit.

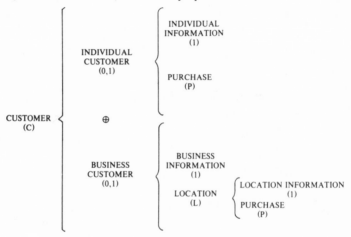

Figure 5.6. Warnier Diagram of same problem.

Clear, understandable documentation is essential in any system. The larger and/or more complex the system is, the greater is the need for exact documentation. Whenever we allow ambiguity to slip into a systems definition, we open a veritable Pandora's box of evils.

In general, when describing data structures, especially complex ones, remember that *a Warnier Diagram always describes a logical data access path for sets and subsets of data.* Thinking of data in terms of access paths at first may be difficult. Indeed, until the advent of data base management systems, we were so accustomed to thinking of data in physical terms that most of us still have great difficulty in breaking away from that mode of thinking.

An example that illustrates our inability to see clearly the differences between logical and physical data structure is our treatment of sequential files. Such files, we have been taught, are inadequate, rigid, and out-of-date. On the other hand, newer file structures, such as hierarchical data bases, are capable of wonderful and miraculous things. In fact, while both statements are true to some extent, they both are misleading. Why? Because most of the files that we have traditionally called sequential are, in fact, hierarchically sequential files, i.e., sorted. Moreover, many of the advantages that are ascribed to hierarchical data base structures also apply, if you think about it, to hierarchically sequential files. For example:

> A data file is made up of detailed records of line item purchases, sorted by product number, customer number, and order number. An order number, customer number, product number, units ordered, sales amount, and date are kept for each line item.

In the traditional view, a file is a file is a file; and the only important thing to consider is that a file is made up of records, and records are made up of fields. We could diagram it as such:

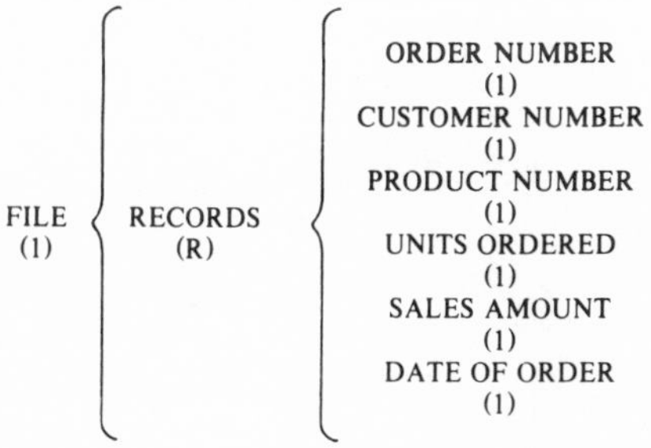

FILE (1) { RECORDS (R) { ORDER NUMBER (1) / CUSTOMER NUMBER (1) / PRODUCT NUMBER (1) / UNITS ORDERED (1) / SALES AMOUNT (1) / DATE OF ORDER (1) }

Figure 5.7. Warnier Diagram of file and records.

However, this would not be a complete logical description of the file in question, because we have failed to treat the hierarchical structure sequence of data access. If we thought of the file only in terms of the previous description, we would miss the fact that the data on this file have been ordered into sets, subsets, and sub-subsets of data:

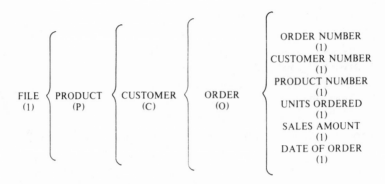

Figure 5.8. More complete diagram of data.

Now our ugly duckling sequential file suddenly has become a beautiful swan-like hierarchical structure. We could even draw a data base diagram just to be in step with the times:

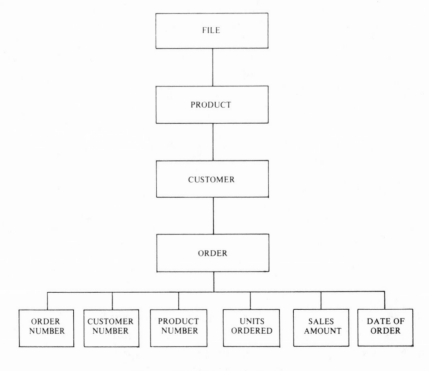

Figure 5.9. Data base diagram.

We could actually reorient our data according to use and availability, as follows:

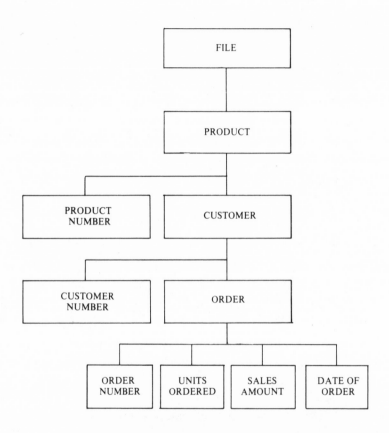

Figure 5.10. Reorientation of data base diagram.

It turns out that it is not only possible to describe complex data structures in a better fashion using Warnier Diagrams, but we can also learn more about data structures once considered self-evident.

One final thought regarding Warnier Diagrams and data structures: Programs can also be thought of as data. Therefore, we can if we desire describe a COBOL source program with a Warnier Diagram:

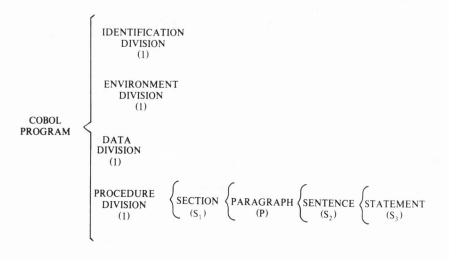

Figure 5.11. Warnier Diagram of a COBOL program.

It's interesting to note that Warnier's L.C.P. (Logical Construction of Programs) methodology[2] is based in part upon the idea of treating the statements (actions) in a program as sets of data structured in a very rigorous manner.

There is simply no way of separating programs or systems from the data they process. The more we know about one, the more we know about the other.

An example contrasting systems requirements with systems architecture

We've absorbed new ideas and terminology at a rapid rate. Let's see if an example can help clarify our discussion. This example is one of the best known to illustrate the difference

---

[2]J.D. Warnier, *Logical Construction of Programs,* 3rd ed., trans. B.M. Flanagan (New York: Van Nostrand Reinhold Co., 1976).

between systems requirements and systems architecture. The example is based on an actual experience that I will relate later. The problem is simple.

Produce a statistical summary report from a series of monthly statistical cards.

Simple problems such as this are nice, in that they allow you to see an entire solution on a single page. A Warnier Diagram of our problem with inputs and outputs would be roughly as follows:

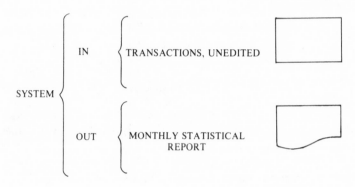

Figure 5.12. Rough Warnier Diagram of simple problem.

Without any discussion of the correct method of systems design, I've found two basic approaches that most people use to solve a problem such as this. Interestingly enough, the choice of approach is usually a function of your having received your programming training in either a scientific/engineering environment, or in a commercial/business data processing environment.

Explanation — The basic programming model that most engineers and scientists learn is to read their data into the machine and to summarize it in a "Big Ole Matrix" (B.O.M.). After all the data have been entered, the matrix is accessed in the order required and the output report produced.

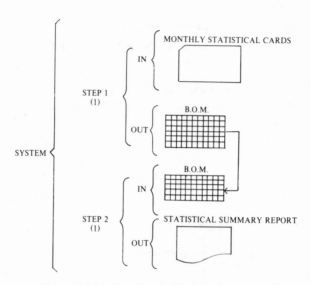

Figure 5.13. Solution 1 (engineer's solution).

Explanation — Like the first solution, the commercial programmer's solution has two steps. However, the first natural step of the business programmer is to sort his data into the desired sequence (structure) of the report, and his second step is to summarize and print at the same time.

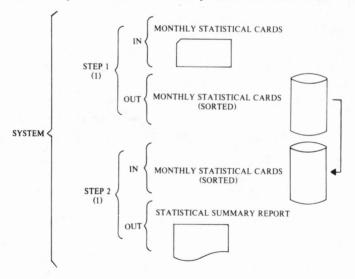

Figure 5.14. Solution 2 (commercial programmer's solution).

This example points out the relationship between architecture and efficiency. Efficiency is a relative term. To talk about efficiency, you need to have at least two correct solutions to the same problem. In this particular case, it's easy to imagine that we can make both solutions work. The next question is: Which one is better? If you answered: It all depends! you were right. Solution 1 tends to be better if there is sufficient real core to contain the entire B.O.M. The second solution is usually better when it is not possible to keep the entire matrix in core at one time. Unfortunately, the point at which the balance tips from one solution to the other is usually not clear. For example, there are a great many programs that have run very efficiently for years using Solution 1 only to become real dogs when someone attempted to convert them to run on a virtual memory system without sufficient core to contain the entire B.O.M.

In general, we find that determining efficiency usually comes down to "depends on" questions. The best solution depends on the volume of transactions, on the distribution of transaction types, or on the frequency of response. However, we must be able to recognize different systems architectures to deal with questions of efficiency. In my experience, I have found that most people suffer from a poverty of models for solving problems. Most of us learn one or two basic programming (or systems) solutions early in our careers; and after that, we proceed to use the same models over and over again to solve all problems, whether they are appropriate or not.

Some ten or twelve years ago, I went with a young associate, who was a bright young fellow with degrees from Massachusetts Institute of Technology and the University of Chicago to call on a client. My associate was an expert in linear programming models, and a pretty fair FORTRAN programmer. In this particular case, our client had a rather large file from which he wanted to produce some frequency distributions: I remember, he wanted to know the number of people by sex, age, height, weight, location, and color of hair, who bought Nutty-Crunchies in Milwaukee.

After about an hour, my associate suddenly announced, "I don't think that we can do your job on our computer!" Naturally, that came as something of a shock to me because I already had a scheme (Solution 2) that I was pretty sure would solve the problem. It also came as something of a shock to our client, mainly because he had been doing the same job for years using only a card sorter and an accounting machine. I quickly adjourned the meeting and took my associate aside, asking as politely as I could, what he meant by saying that we couldn't solve the problem on our computer.

Well, it turns out that my friend had only one basic scheme for solving problems of this nature. His approach was Solution 1. While we were discussing the problem, he had mentally computed the size of the matrix we would need to contain all the data for the report. Since the size of the B.O.M. required exceeded the available core of our machine, he concluded, correctly from his standpoint, that our computer simply wasn't big enough for the job. Technically, he was right, but only in the narrow sense. My friend was suffering from a poverty of problem-solving models.

Over the years, I have had to explain Solution 2 to many engineering types and in turn explain Solution 1 to an equal number of business programmers. Only as I began to understand the difference between systems requirements and systems architecture did I realize that most of us keep solving the same problem over and over again independent of whether the problem lends itself to the same systems architecture as the last problem we solved. Unfortunately, when we meet a really different problem, we usually come up short.

6

THE APPLICATION
OF LOGIC
TO SYSTEMS BUILDING

A few years ago, one of my little girls, who was then less than two years old, was having a tantrum; and nothing that my wife or I could do would satisfy her. She seemed to want a drink of ice water, but whenever we gave it to her, she became upset. She also became upset when we tried to take the glass away. We finally concluded that what she wanted was ice water with ice but no ice. We've laughed about that incident for years now, and we use it to describe any situation in which someone wants to have his cake and eat it, too.

My daughter is older now and understands she cannot have ice water with ice but no ice. In fact, she even can take my own statements and show me where they lead, especially if the logical conclusion means an extra treat or a later bed-time for her. My point has to do with logic. Even little children understand logic, and yet logic for many people remains a cold, remote subject, something to be studied only by mathematicians, philosophers, or electronic engineers. In fact, logic actually rules the world; none of us can escape its use or bend its laws even a little. That which is truly illogical is unthinkable; logic is neither hard nor easy; it is simply unavoidable.

Aristotle is credited with discovering formal logic in the fifth century B.C., and the rules he established are as valid today as they were two thousand years ago, and perhaps are even more important. Today, however, we usually call formal logic by a number of different names: mathematical logic, boolean algebra, switching theory, and set theory, just to name a few. All the miraculous things computers do are accomplished with only logic to guide them. Indeed, all computing rests ultimately on a few logical rules carried on at mind-boggling speeds.

For myself, the problem with logic was not that I lacked appreciation for its power or importance, it was just that I simply couldn't figure out how to use logic consistently on practical problems. Over the years, I had had any number of courses on logic or set theory or symbolic logic, all basically derived from the same laws; but for the life of me, I was never able to systematically use that logical knowledge to solve practical problems. As a programmer and analyst, I had difficulty applying logic — an embarrassing admission, since most of the problems faced by analysts and programmers are really only problems of applied logic. My only comfort, if you could call it that, stemmed from the realization that none of the other programmers or analysts I knew had developed any systematic method of applying logic to writing programs or systems either. This no longer needs to be true — the following pages will show you how logic can be systematically applied to structured problem solving.

Plenty of good books have been written on logic; so, without delving too deeply, let me try now to demonstrate how logic can be applied to constructing well-defined programs or systems. Suppose we had the following problem:

- A file contains the data on each patient in a hospital.

- Write a program that computes and prints a bill for each active patient in the hospital.

Let's see how we can develop a structured solution that will meet the logical requirements of the problem, without knowing exactly how to compute a patient's bill, or without knowing even the exact format for the bill.

Begin by drawing some simple logical pictures called Venn Diagrams (after the 19th century English mathematician). First, we draw a diagram showing the relationship of all the patients to the hospital.

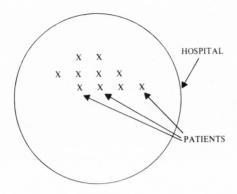

Figure 6.1. Venn Diagram of hospital problem.

Our set, hospital, is made up of members called patients. The logical job at hand is to produce certain things (bills), not for every member (patient) of the hospital set, but only for a subset of the members of the hospital, the active patients. That diagram would appear as follows:

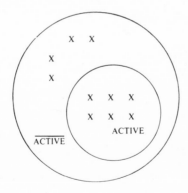

Figure 6.2. Venn Diagram showing subset of hospital members.

The small oval within the large one represents the subset of all the active patients. From logic, we know that everything outside that smaller logical oval is made up of patients who are nonactive (ACTIVE).

There are, naturally, a vast number of ways to treat this problem from a design standpoint, but let's use the most general one. If we examined each patient within the hospital, and if we could determine from the patient's data whether he or she was active, then we could make sure we would do only the right things. To determine clearly what those things are, we need to draw yet another logical chart, called a Karnaugh Map. Because of the problem's simplicity, the diagram is a trivial one.

ACTIVE PATIENT	COMPUTE AND PRINT BILL
$\overline{\text{ACTIVE PATIENT}}$	SKIP

Figure 6.3. Karnaugh Map of problem.

A correct logical solution, then, would be one in which the right logical actions took place on the right sets of data under the right conditions. How would that look? Probably as follows:

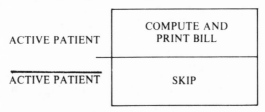

Figure 6.4. Logical solution (Warnier Diagram) of problem.

The Warnier Diagram portrays the logical solution very simply.

But because we are able to draw a clear Warnier Diagram that solves the problem doesn't mean that we're finished or that we've arrived at a solution. We still have to convert this diagram into a program . . . or do we? Perhaps the structure of the solution can be made to look like the Warnier Diagram already derived. How? Let's add some features to our Warnier Diagram:

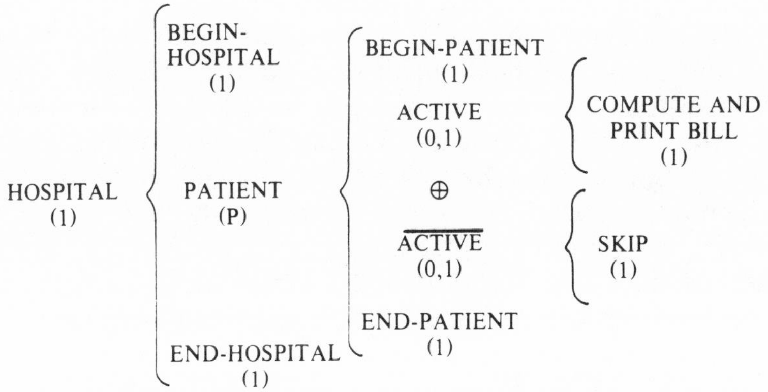

HOSPITAL (1) {
   BEGIN-HOSPITAL (1)

   PATIENT (P) {
      BEGIN-PATIENT (1)

      ACTIVE (0,1) { COMPUTE AND PRINT BILL (1)

      ⊕

      $\overline{\text{ACTIVE}}$ (0,1) { SKIP (1)

      END-PATIENT (1)

   END-HOSPITAL (1)
}

Figure 6.5. Warnier Diagram with beginning and end blocks.

All we've actually done is to add a beginning and an end block to each logical bracket. Initially, students find this step a waste of time; however, the blocks serve an important function in producing correct programs, as you will see later.

The immediate thought of most programmers and analysts is that the above structure is not the right one. "In programming," they say, "we deal with files and records, not sets of data. It all looks very simple when you show your logical description that way, but that's not the way we typically write programs!" And they are right. Although we traditionally have not written programs to conform to the logical structure of their solution, let's see if we can do so in the above case. What do we need to do to complete our solutions? We have the age-old problems of reading data and writing out results. Let's find the appropriate places to do so in our solution.

First, suppose we select a file structure for our data. We require one in which we can access the first patient in the hospital and each subsequent patient until we receive a message saying that we have processed all of the patients. In that way, we can be assured of processing all patients. Since any number of methods of physical organization will do, why don't we choose the simplest one — a sequential structure in which one patient's data follows another? Let's assume further that there is only one physical record per patient in the hospital files.

If we have P patients in the hospital file, to solve our logical problem, we will have to get data from the file P + 1 times: one time per patient record, plus one time to know we are at the end of data. In looking at the Warnier Diagram above, we might be interested in just which blocks are done P times and which are done just once. BEGIN-PATIENT and END-PATIENT are both done P times, and BEGIN-HOSPITAL and END-HOSPITAL are each done one time. Let's choose BEGIN-HOSPITAL and END-PATIENT as the appropriate places to do our physical reading of data.

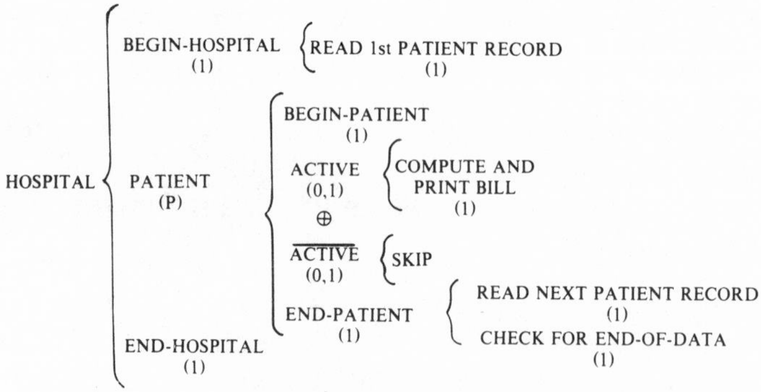

Figure 6.6. Warnier Diagram with physical reading
of data shown.

Our logical solution now is coming closer to becoming a physical one as well. Of course, we still need to add other things to make our logical solution completely physical, but I'll leave that to the reader. We've accomplished what we wanted to do, which was to show a straightforward method of transforming a logical solution into a program. By the way, the end product of this process always will be a structured program. Why? You might reply, "Simple logic, simple structured program. Nice, but so what? I'll bet it doesn't work on a complex logical problem!" Suppose we see!

Problem — The Human Resources Department of a state government manages a number of state hospitals. For each active patient in this case, one of two types of bill is produced, depending upon whether the patient is covered by insurance or not. For nonactive patients, bills are produced only for insured patients. This procedure is done for each hospital, and totals are produced by hospital and for the department.

In this case, our Venn Diagram and Karnaugh Map are considerably more important:

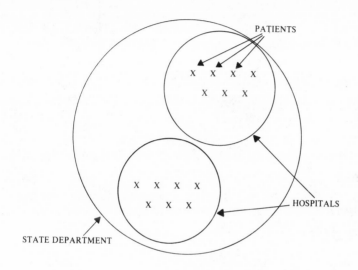

Figure 6.7. Venn Diagram of complex logical problem.

While the patients still are basic elements and still are members of hospital data sets, the hospitals themselves are now members (or subsets) of a higher level set — the state department.

What about the logical processing (using a Karnaugh Map)? It, too, is slightly more complex per patient.

	INSURED	$\overline{\text{INSURED}}$
ACTIVE	COMPUTE AND PRINT INSURANCE BILL	COMPUTE AND PRINT REGULAR BILL
$\overline{\text{ACTIVE}}$	COMPUTE AND PRINT INSURANCE BILL	SKIP

Figure 6.8. Karnaugh Map of same problem.

There is more than one way to solve the problem, depending upon which of two logical variables we choose to test first.

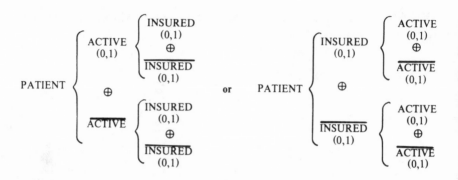

Figure 6.9. Two solutions to the problem.

By constructing the solution in either order, we get the same correct results. Which is better? After examining the Karnaugh Map above (Figure 6.8), we can see that making the test on IN-SURED versus INSURED first requires fewer steps.

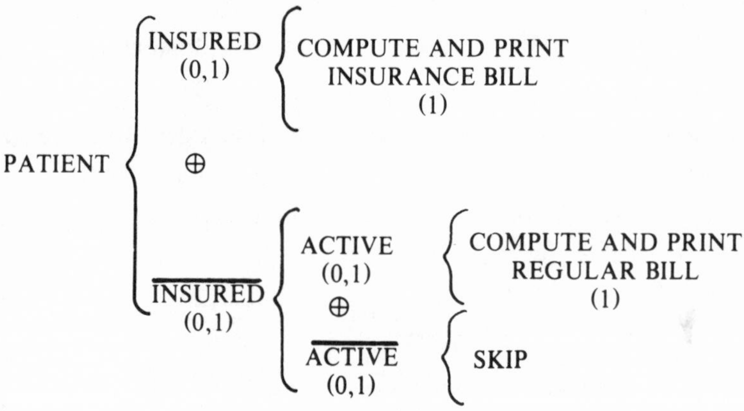

$$
\text{PATIENT}
\begin{cases}
\begin{array}{l}\text{INSURED}\\(0,1)\end{array}
\begin{cases}\text{COMPUTE AND PRINT}\\\text{INSURANCE BILL}\\(1)\end{cases}\\
\oplus\\
\begin{array}{l}\overline{\text{INSURED}}\\(0,1)\end{array}
\begin{cases}
\begin{array}{l}\text{ACTIVE}\\(0,1)\end{array}
\begin{cases}\text{COMPUTE AND PRINT}\\\text{REGULAR BILL}\\(1)\end{cases}\\
\oplus\\
\begin{array}{l}\overline{\text{ACTIVE}}\\(0,1)\end{array}
\begin{cases}\text{SKIP}\end{cases}
\end{cases}
\end{cases}
$$

Figure 6.10. Testing INSURED logical variable first.

But we've solved only part of our problem. The whole problem involves computing (or not computing) the proper bill for each patient in each hospital. Let's see how that fits:

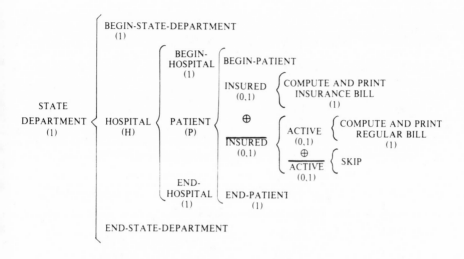

Figure 6.11. Diagram of computing bills for all patients.

In this case, the additional complexity of the problem introduced new logical levels, both at the top and near the bottom of the diagram. However, the increased complexity has not created a complex or unstructured logical solution. In fact, our solution is still simple enough to allow us to verify that all the logical operations spelled out in the problem are actually done properly in the solution.

A note is required regarding the data structure necessary for this problem. While our original file simply had a record for each patient in one hospital, we must now access our data for each hospital in which the data are broken down by patient. Again, any number of structures would do, but for the sake of simplicity, we again will choose a sequential file. We will use a hierarchically sequential file, with the hierarchy being set (state department), subset (hospital), and sub-subset (patient). To accomplish this, we need to establish a key and sort the data. With this new data structure, we need to put the physical reading of our input as follows:

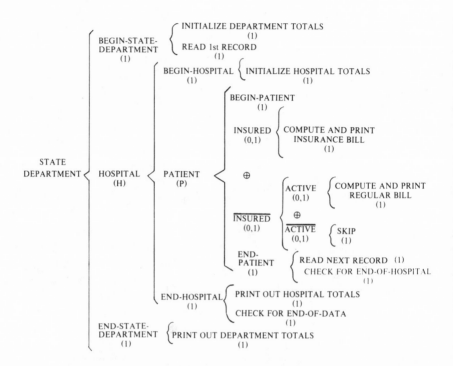

Figure 6.12. Hierarchically sequential file.

If the hierarchical data structure correctly matches the output, then producing the correct logical output becomes a much easier job. And since simplicity is one of our goals, we should strive to develop systems in which the data can be thought of as being hierarchically structured.

Logic is a cornerstone of structured systems design. Therefore, it should not be surprising at all to find the correspondence between the concepts underlying logic and those underlying systems and program development. In recent years, a whole methodology has built up around a few basic concepts: function, alternation, repetition, and sequence (see Figures 6.13a and 6.13b). Over a decade ago, it was demonstrated that any program could be developed using only a couple of these basic forms of construction; the feasibility of doing structured programming grew entirely from the knowledge that these forms were sufficient to attack any problem.

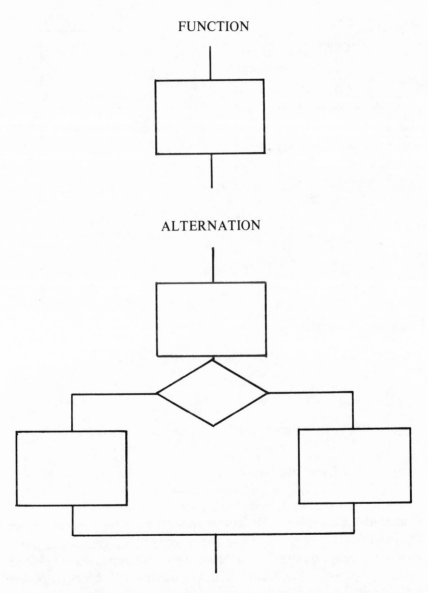

Figure 6.13a. Basic forms of construction for program and systems development: function and alternation.

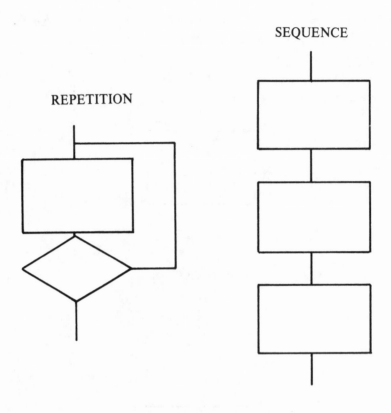

Figure 6.13b. Basic forms of construction for program and
systems development: repetition and sequence.

As we have used just these logical structures for building
programs and systems, we have also realized that these basic
forms are analogous to the fundamental building blocks of logic.
And the more we learn about the application of these techniques,
the easier it becomes to utilize the vast body of knowledge about
logic and logical systems that has existed for centuries. Until recently, however, that transfer of knowledge was blocked by our
inability to see how to draw the appropriate connections between
logic and systems solutions to problems.

Solving complex logical problems is daily fare for a systems analyst. His ability to help users understand their own problems, and to state their problems clearly in a rigorous, logical manner is one of the analyst's main strengths. In this sense, the analyst acts as a catalyst or midwife, because he can't solve the user's problem for him, no matter how much he would like to. He can analyze, he can restate, he can educate; but, ultimately, it is the user who must finally define the requirements.

In one sense, a system can be regarded simply as a single, extremely large program. Whereas a program may have to deal with only a few logical variables, a system may have to deal with thousands. Because systems contain so many variables, we have tended to break them into a great many pieces in the hope that we could somehow deal with all the millions of possible cases a few at a time. Today, we are less frightened of dealing with a system as a whole than we were a few years ago, because structuring has made it possible actually to see the systems forest for all the logical trees. Suppose we look at a logical model of a general system and consider its logical requirements. For example:

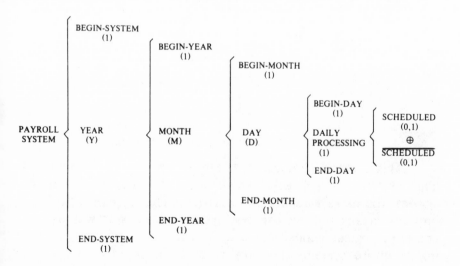

Figure 6.14. Logical model of a system.

In Figure 6.14, we can see a natural, logical hierarchy in which certain things (actions) are done a certain number of times. Clearly, with a picture like this, it becomes easy to isolate where in the system to place the production of various time-independent activities, such as producing control registers (end of day), producing payroll checks (end of month), and producing W-2 documents (end of year). In fact, most accounting systems are time-dependent in one sense or another.

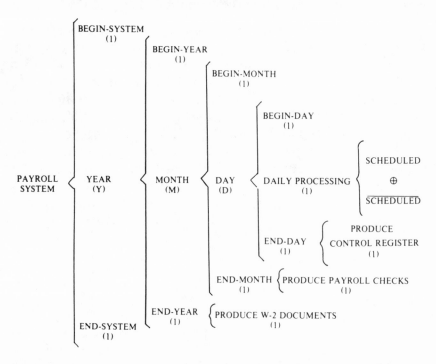

Figure 6.15. Systems chart for payroll system.

This method of documentation allows an understanding of large systems as well as of small ones. Indeed, the larger the system, the more valuable the approach. The rigor that structure imposes means that we can test systems designs as well as programs for logical inconsistencies. For the most part, the structuring of entire systems has only recently emerged as a possible documenting approach. Previously, we have tended to "chop" a large system into pieces more or less arbitrarily or along organizational lines. In a great many cases, this has only made the problem worse, not better.

The systems chart above (Figure 6.15) is the refinement of a series of attempts at designing overall systems. It was something of a shock to find similar systems levels charts appearing in widely different applications. The outlines have always been there; however, it is easier to understand and communicate how both the big and the small pieces of a system fit together.

At first glance, it is sometimes difficult to see how to implement a system such as the one above, so we often have to convert it into one we can deal with operationally, such as a daily system. We can think of the hierarchical system as shown above, or we can collapse the hierarchy into the following structure that makes it easier to see how we would operate.

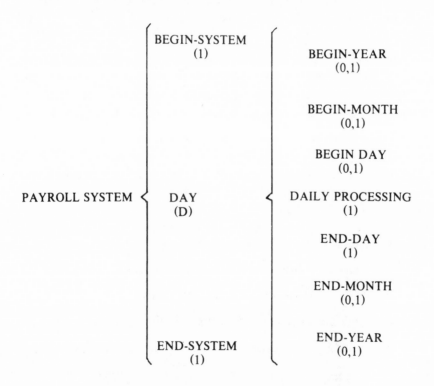

Figure 6.16. Structure of system's operation.

In fact, many report-generator-type languages such as RPG use this approach to deal with all processing problems. We've found generally that there are any number of logically equivalent systems descriptions that will insure that the right sets of actions get accomplished at the right times. Depending upon the environment (manual or semiautomated, on-line or batch), we may need to modify our approach. The result, however, is the same: a logically correct system.

Often, the new systems analyst will rebel against completely working out a logically correct system. Moreover, the user may desire more flexibility. However, we have become more and more convinced that a great many of the operational difficulties with existing systems are a direct result of incorrect systems design. Historically, we have turned over to user or operations scheduling, complex systems considerations that we could not (or would not) handle. Now, we can see these problem areas for what they really are: problems of logical systems organization.

Structured systems design supplies us with tools to deal directly with problems of logical systems organization, provided we have the necessary training and experience. An advantage of using this approach is that we can see the big picture all at once.

Let's take an example. Suppose you were a new systems analyst faced with the problem of organizing various known requirements of a system. At this point, all you have defined are a series of systems outputs and the desired frequency at which they are to be produced:

- Order Status Report (daily)
- Order Status Summary Report (daily)
- Customer Status Report (monthly)
- Product Production Statistics (monthly)
- Order Processing Statistics (monthly, yearly)

Since you need a place to put the various pieces you have defined, the logical systems description above provides a framework. For example, where should you put the Order Status Summary Report? That's right, in the END-DAY process. And the Customer Status Report? In the END-MONTH, naturally, and so on (see Figure 6.17).

By having a logically complete (and correct) systems structure, the analyst has a conceptual framework in which to put pieces of the puzzle as he figures them out. If it is true, as we believe, that all good systems look a lot alike, having a correct conceptual framework is a *major* asset for an analyst.

After we've examined the hierarchical structure of the various outputs (as shown in the system chart above), we often find that we want to reorder the sequence in which the various outputs are produced. Or we may want to merge two or more sequences of actions into one (if they have the same basic hierarchical structure). But as long as the various reports in this case are required at the present frequencies, the sequence of their logical segments is fixed.

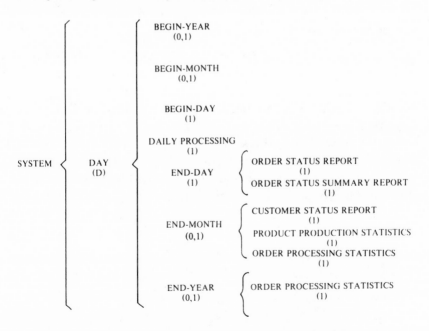

Figure 6.17. System structure given outputs and frequencies.

Notice that one output, Order Processing Status, must be produced at the end of each month as well as at the end, of the year (presumably a summary version) and is shown in two places. In fact, we will treat these logically as two different reports even though they are produced by the same program. However, since the same program (set of actions) operates on a different set of data, that makes it necessary to show it in two logical places — redundancy is no sin.

In general, we would like to be able to respond to user requirements without any prejudice toward one systems architecture over another. For example, we would like to avoid committing ourselves to an automated system over a manual system or to an on-line system over a batch system. In fact, we would like as much as possible to let the systems requirements direct us. One way of doing this is to help the user understand his requirements in terms of "periods of use." If a report will only be used quarterly, it should only be produced quarterly. If a twenty-four hour response time is sufficient, there is no need to put that portion of the system on-line.

I remember a quote that is particularly appropriate. A friend of mine, Bob Courtney from IBM, once remarked at a Data Security Meeting, "Time is nature's way of keeping everything from happening at once." By using Warnier Diagrams to identify when things need to be done, and by knowing when information is required, the systems analyst is provided a neat and powerful way in which to partition (and integrate) his system at a high level, especially when that logical model insures that all outputs will be produced at the right times.

7 USING STRUCTURED SYSTEMS DESIGN

I was talking one day with a systems manager for one of our clients when the question arose of how good are Warnier Diagrams. He related this incident: It seems that during the course of a review session, the manager had asked to see the programmer's Warnier Diagram of the program in question. He made some criticisms, at which point the programmer replied angrily, "But you haven't even been to the structured systems design class!" To which the manager replied, "You're right, and I realize that I don't know how to make a good Warnier Diagram from scratch; however, the great advantage of these charts is that I can recognize a bad one when I see it!"

There is a moral to this story: Good communication is a two-edged sword. If you communicate more clearly, people can understand you better, but you also had better be prepared for more criticism. However, it is far better to have people criticize your intermediate thinking than your end product. We have found that it is more important to be clear than it is to be right, for if you are clearly wrong, someone will tell you. However, if you are obscurely right, you may never know it.

My manager friend was intelligent enough to recognize that he himself didn't have the training to prepare a good Warnier chart. Many people are not so observant. Because Warnier Diagrams are so easy to understand, many people imagine that constructing a good one is a simple task. With experience, they do become easier and easier to put together — but never simple.

We talk a great deal about the process of designing and discuss ways to appreciate its importance in systems building. Nowhere is the importance of design more evident than when you attempt to carefully describe a logical process using a Warnier Diagram.

How do you begin? Is there some sort of cookbook to use as a foolproof method? If not, is the process of design even teachable?

Some general rules about constructing a Warnier Diagram can be taught, but they certainly do not constitute a cookbook. Let's take a simple example similar to one seen before. Suppose a user calls me and says, "Look, I need a Project Status Report to keep track of all the work in the shop."

Step 1:   Use the Warnier Diagram to sketch the overall problem.

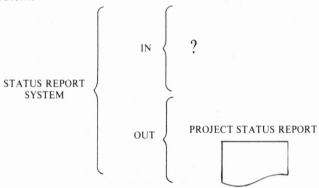

Figure 7.1. Warnier Diagram showing overall problem.

At this point, any good analyst will probe as deeply as he can without offending the user. As stated before, we want to get the user to think in terms of the outputs of the systems and especially of their uses. However, time after time, we find users developing what they think are the solutions to their problems. (I know of one organization that had actually designed and purchased the input forms before they had even talked with a systems analyst to determine the desired output.)

In the requirements stage, the analyst has to act much like a doctor in diagnosing an illness. He must take careful note of why the patient has come in, and he must see if the patient's conclusion is correct. Like the doctor, the analyst must start from where the user is. The analyst cannot browbeat, intimidate, or humiliate the user at the outset. The user has a problem and thinks the analyst can help him or he wouldn't be there. So *the analyst has to guide the user from where he is to where he ought to be to solve his problems.*

Returning to our original problem, you can probe the user with questions such as:

What are you going to use this report for?

What kind of status are you concerned with?

Then, when you are convinced that the user understands his problem,

Step 2: Identify the structure of the output of the system.

You can begin by producing a Warnier Diagram of the hierarchy of the desired output, sketching the overall format of what the user wants.

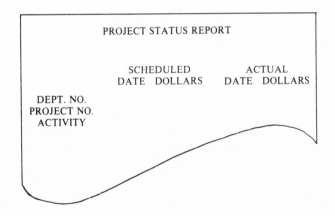

Figure 7.2. Sketch of overall format.

It is important to be very specific about the output, because most people have great difficulty with abstractions. This is one reason why systems work comes hard. At any rate, the next task in this step is to develop the logical data hierarchy for the report desired:

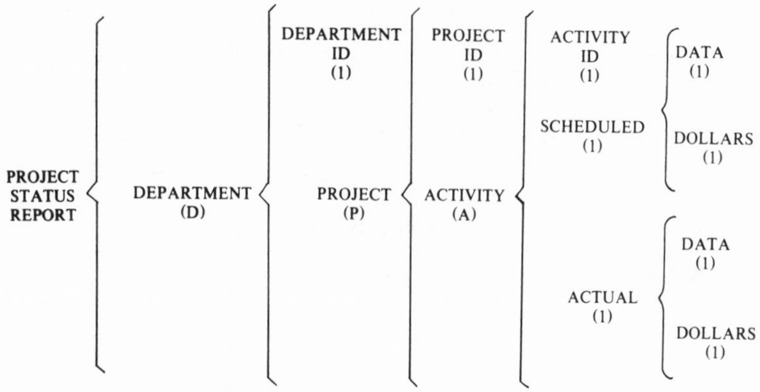

Figure 7.3. Warnier Diagram of logical data hierarchy.

Adding this further definition to our systems chart is usually not a good idea until the user is fairly certain he has what he wants. As you talk to the user, it becomes clear that he has omitted some things from this diagram. For one thing, he hasn't told you anything about the frequency of the output. Clearly, daily is too often for a report such as this; but, on the other hand, monthly may not be frequent enough to allow for corrective action. Suppose you determine that this report should be produced monthly, but that for project management purposes, a Trouble Report should be produced weekly. So you change your systems diagram as follows:

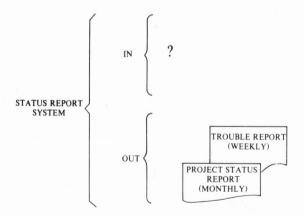

Figure 7.4. Revised systems diagram.

The Trouble Report has the following format:

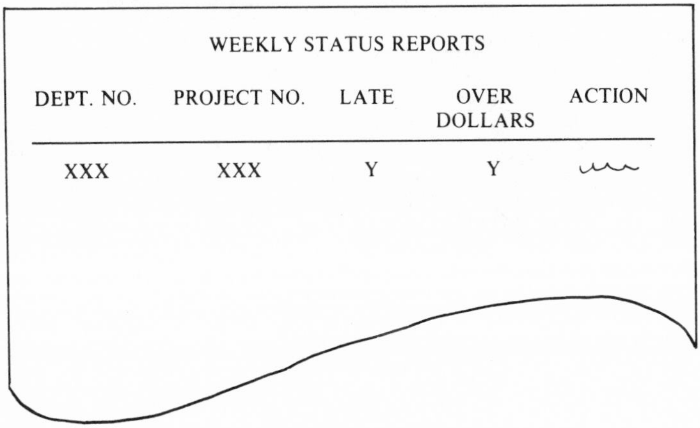

WEEKLY STATUS REPORTS				
DEPT. NO.	PROJECT NO.	LATE	OVER DOLLARS	ACTION
XXX	XXX	Y	Y	‿‿‿

Figure 7.5. Trouble Report.

In discussing this report, we find that a list of projects is derived, with the most serious problems appearing first. The structure looks as follows:

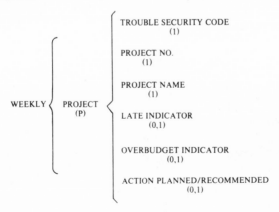

Figure 7.6. Warnier Diagram of Trouble Report.

Since we have determined all the outputs possible for the moment, the next step is to consider the logical data needed in this system.

Step 3: Identify the logical data base for the system.

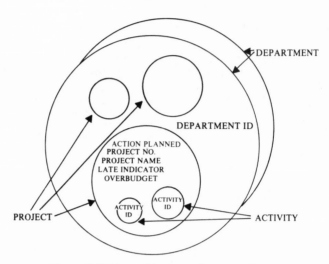

Figure 7.7. Venn Diagram of system data.

A minimum amount of apparent information is required in a system. This is usually a good point to summarize what we know about that data. We'll show the logical sum or overlap of the data needed for the two reports already defined.

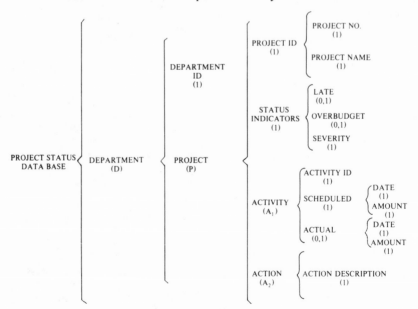

Figure 7.8. Warnier Diagram.

The data items appearing on the far right side of this diagram can be thought of as undefined elements that must be either further defined or captured as input. With the exception of the status indicators, we can consider those data on the right to be input. However, the status indicators are a different story. Let's see how we might assign the status severity indicator. (See Figure 7.9 below.)

From this analysis, we see an interesting thing emerge: The STATUS SEVERITY CODE is a data item that is derived from other data (i.e., LATE and OVERBUDGET). We may find, therefore, that we do not want to store the severity code, but rather to generate it just before we produce the weekly report. In data base terminology, severity code is a "derived" or "virtual" data element.

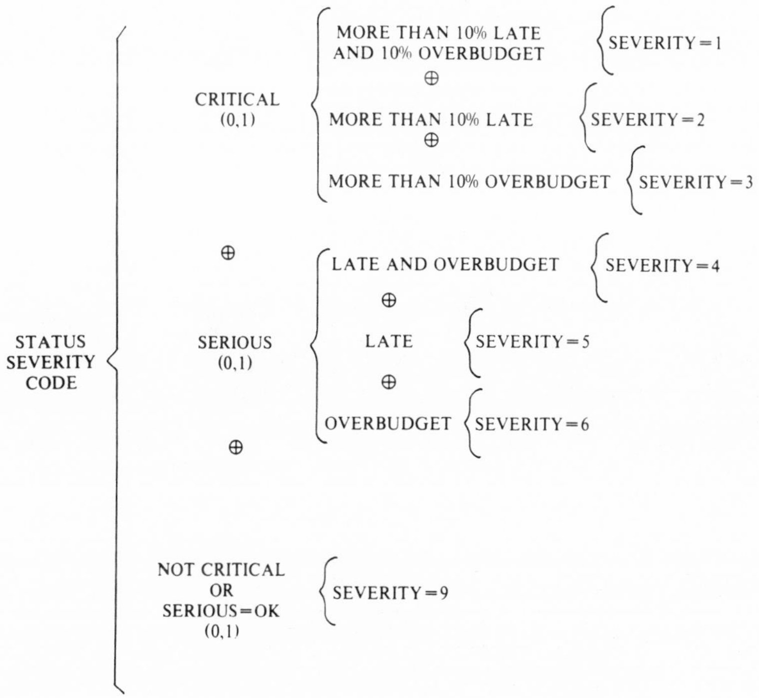

Figure 7.9. Analysis of status severity indicator.

Now we begin to reach the heart of the analysis, the data elements LATE and OVERBUDGET. Let's take the easy one first.

PROJECT OVERBUDGET {
- TOTAL PROJECTED DOLLARS > TOTAL SCHEDULED DOLLARS { OVERBUDGET=TRUE
- ⊕
- TOTAL PROJECTED DOLLARS ⩽ TOTAL SCHEDULED DOLLARS { OVERBUDGET=FALSE

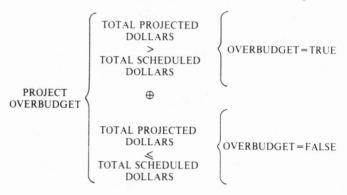

Figure 7.10. Data analysis of OVERBUDGET.

Now we need to go further.

TOTAL SCHEDULED DOLLARS { = Σ ACTIVITY SCHEDULED DOLLARS (FOR ALL ACTIVITIES IN PROJECT)

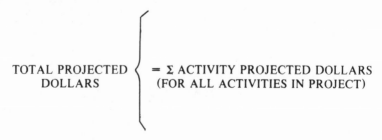

Figure 7.11. Further analysis of data item.

Again, we've reached a data item, ACTIVITY SCHEDULED DOLLARS, that we know to be input. But what about TOTAL PROJECTED DOLLARS?

TOTAL PROJECTED DOLLARS { = Σ ACTIVITY PROJECTED DOLLARS (FOR ALL ACTIVITIES IN PROJECT)

Figure 7.12. Further analysis of data item.

How did we come up with the total projected dollars for the project? We began by considering actual dollars by activity and discovered that the method would reveal which projects were critical only after we were finished with the entire project — which is a little late! In this case, we will have to return to our original report and add projected dates and dollars.

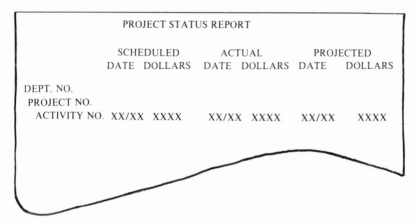

Figure 7.13. Revised Project Status Report.

Thus, our analysis of exactly what data we needed led us to introduce data that are terribly important, but not anticipated. This is a normal occurrence. It is just the outcome we want. It is far better to discover an omission early, while we can still correct it. Now dealing with LATE, we have more problems:

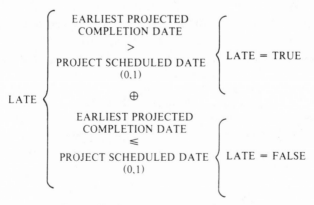

Figure 7.14. Data analysis of LATE.

We can see the origin of PROJECT SCHEDULED DATE, but what about the EARLIEST PROJECTED COMPLETION DATE (EPCD)? How do we determine it?

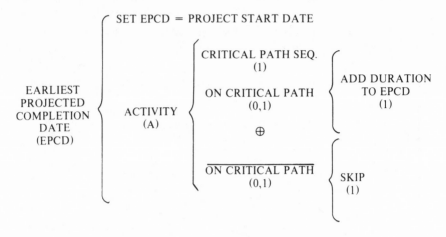

Figure 7.15. Further analysis of data item.

This chart says that to know the EARLIEST PROJECTED COMPLETION DATE, sort the activities by the EARLIEST PROJECTED START DATE and sum the duration of those activities on any critical path.

At this point, many users probably are saying, "Hey, wait a minute! I didn't say anything about a project network; I just wanted a simple Project Status Report." Would they be right? Partially. What they would like and what they need to do a good job are often different things. Dollars differ from dates in that dollars can be summed to give the total cost for the project. The only dates for which this is true are those on one of the project's critical paths.

After this analysis, our logical data base has more information (see Figure 7.16). The actual placement of certain data structures has been rearranged, because it seems reasonable to put data elements following the data from which they are computed.

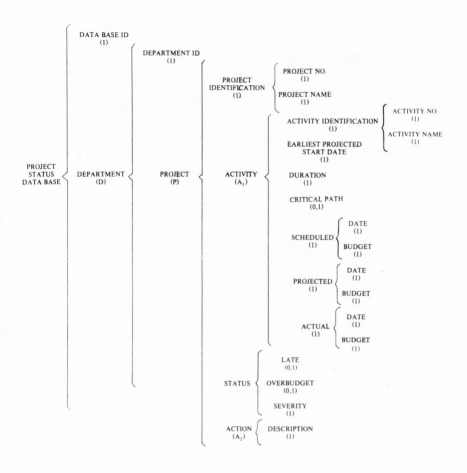

Figure 7.16. Logical data base with additional information.

By studying how the data can (or ought to) be organized from a logical standpoint, we begin to understand more clearly exactly what is required.

Step 4: Place the systems requirements into a basic systems flow. (See Figure 7.17.)

Suppose we use one of our basic systems models to figure out how to capture the essence of the user's desires:

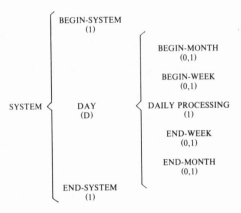

Figure 7.17. Basic systems flow.

We can clearly insert the correct output at the right time:

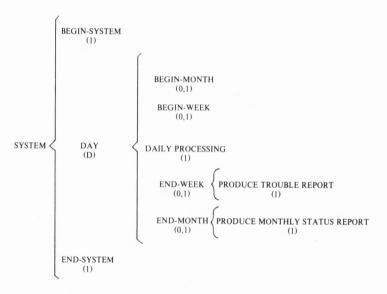

Figure 7.18. Systems flow with outputs specified.

That gives us a consistent place to put the principal output of the system. We know, though, that we will have to derive some of the data required for the Trouble Report and to sort it into sequence by severity.

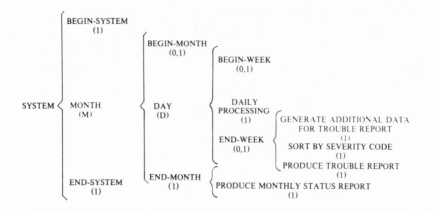

Figure 7.19. Sequenced data for the Trouble Report.

If we could generate the data as specified in the logical data base, then we would produce the output required with little trouble. But that's a big "if." The next step, with a general picture of the system, is:

Step 5: Look to see if the data required already exists in the organization with the correct units and timing.

One of the reasons that so many fragmented systems exist today is that new applications were not carefully integrated with ongoing systems as they evolved. To make our little problem easier, assume that, after considerable research, we find the instance of a project network system that already maintains, on a weekly basis, the critical path, earliest start, and duration information by project and by activity. We decide to simply access this data rather than to recompute it. Because this needs to be done at the end of each week after updating the project network files, we reflect this in our systems flow. (See Figure 7.20.)

"Packaging" the system is the process of specifying which logical elements get grouped into programs or procedures, and so on. However, it is worth noting now that you don't need or want to make the commitment to packaging too early. All that is indicated in the chart in Figure 7.20 is that certain steps should be done in a certain sequence. In fact, it is possible to combine the various elements in END-WEEK processing in a number of ways. For example, at the extreme side, as in Figure 7.21, we could combine the bottom four elements into a single process.

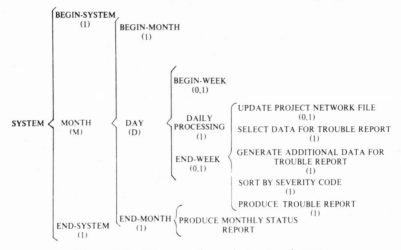

Figure 7.20. Diagram of a project network system.

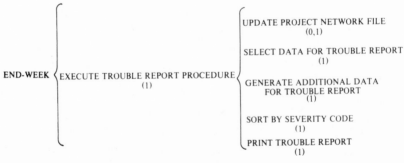

Figure 7.21. Process chart of END-WEEK.

As a matter of fact, the question of whether all this becomes one program or several programs depends upon a number of external factors, computer size, programming standards, and the like. The thing to emphasize is that logically the problem is the same, independent of the packaging. In design, we want to keep as many of our options open as possible. From a logical standpoint, however, doing things in a specific order makes a big difference. We cannot generate the additional data until we have obtained such information as the critical path indicator and duration. Neither can we sort until we have generated the severity code. We must become more like engineers and architects and develop logical, clean designs that flow simply.

After establishing a logical data base and a basic strategy for obtaining this information, what's the next step in structuring our system? It involves determining what will cause the logical data base to change:

> *Step 6: Attempt to identify what real world events will affect the logical data base and how.*

We know from our previous analysis the minimum data needed to meet the user's output requirements. Now we need to consider exactly what things can affect that data. To start, consider the following chart:

EVENT	WHAT DATA	WHEN

Figure 7.22. Event analysis chart.

This chart indicates that we need to know all of the real world events that can affect our data base, including when each occurs and what data it affects. To reach this point, we work backwards from the logical data phase that tells just which sets of data we need to capture and maintain. For example, from our earlier chart, we know that we need data by department, by project, and by activity. Within the category "activity," we need data on scheduled, projected, and actual dates and dollars.

A word of warning at this point: One of our most common problems in getting users and analysts to strictly follow this approach is their desire to guess about the future. It is very hard to get people to settle for just the information that they know they need. Time after time, we hear experienced people saying, "Well, we might as well put X in there because we know we're going to need it someday." However, someday may never come; and if it does, the likelihood will be that we have collected the wrong information. Even if we haven't erred in collecting information, it won't be right if we haven't been using and maintaining the data, and data which are not used will not be correct.

Anyway, given that we have the strength of will to resist collecting a lot of data the system doesn't require, we then ask which events in the real world affect departments? projects? activities? Organizations do change, if only slowly, so we must provide for adding, modifying, and deleting departments. We should not be allowed to delete a department unless all of their projects are either completed, terminated, or reassigned. On the other hand, we don't need to put a department on the file unless they have at least one project.

How about projects? The same thing is true. Projects are added, modified, and deleted. Moreover, they have subsidiary activities, so the same general rules pertain to deleting projects as to departments, i.e., all of the activities should have terminated or been completed before we can delete a project. On the other hand, we may want to add a project without any activities, just for budgeting purposes. (However, would this make any sense from a project status standpoint?)

The same thinking applies to activities as well. We would need to identify all of the various events that can affect activities and how they would affect activities. We might never want to delete an activity after it had been placed on the file, so that even if its duration were set to zero, we would know that we had guessed wrong about the need for certain activities.

Most of the events that affect our data base will occur in the area of modifications to activities, followed closely in frequency by modifications to projects. At this stage, we suggest that you think of all the things that can happen to the data base, including such events as completion, termination, reestimating, and rescheduling. . . . *Rescheduling?* But we don't have any output that reflects rescheduling! Right! What do we do about it? We go back and see how to fit it in.

To avoid surprises, we must watch for potential errors in a systems design process. I remember seeing a classification of typical kinds of errors into four causes: clerical, consistency, communication, and completeness. Of the four, errors in communication and in completeness hurt the most. We can generally solve problems of clerical and consistency errors, *if we know what the problem actually is.* However, if we fail to obtain the right parameters, no amount of technical genius is apt to help us very much. By the real world changes, we can improve both the communication and the completeness of the systems design.

Step 7: Place logical updating actions into basic systems hierarchy.

We can suppose that our event analysis leads to a list of actions having to do with updating the various logical pieces of data in the data base. The next step, then, involves placing those logical updating actions in the correct location within the systems chart. For example, suppose that we decided to accept and edit all information immediately, but actually update project and activity data weekly before the production of the Trouble Report, and update department information only monthly before the Monthly Status Report.

For the moment, let's leave the design alone with the logical steps already specified. After considering where we are and how quickly we've reached this point, you must realize that we're doing all this on paper. As a matter of fact, this is about the point at which something unexpected usually happens. Typically, if the user for whom we've been working isn't reassigned, then somebody changes the definition, or we discover something rather important from just thinking about the problem in greater detail.

For our project, we have reached the point where the user, with our help, suddenly discovers that we're missing an important piece of information. "You know," he says, "we really need another set of dates and dollars in addition to scheduled,

projected, and actual; we need revised dates and dollars!'' Of
course, he's right. To have a meaningful project status system,
you must have the ability to change the schedule as you learn
what the real system will look like. On the other hand, you need
to remember what you orginally projected, because that will help
you see what was faulty in your original planning.

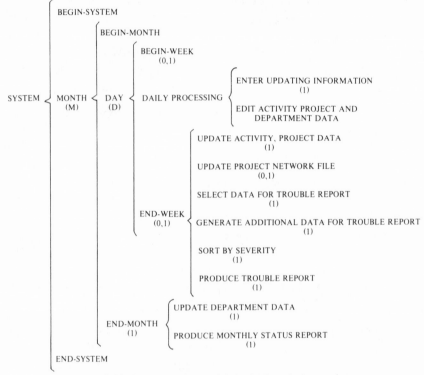

Figure 7.23. Systems chart with logical updating actions.

Now we see that we need to revise our system — and we
haven't even gotten it into programming. As a matter of fact,
maintenance of a systems design begins nearly as soon as you get
the first design down on paper. Often people forget; sometimes
they choose not to remember; sometimes things just change. No
matter, for in most cases we simply have to take their new requirements into account. Clearly, this is not always possible.
Sometimes we must say to the user, "We can't make that
change to this version of the system; however, we'll start work-

ing on it as soon as we get the current (first) version of the system installed." But in most cases, changing is not catastrophic, but failing to produce a correct system is.

Suppose we want to make a change to the systems design. How do we incorporate it into our current systems design? The answer is: *Start at the beginning of the systems procedure and go through the same steps with this new requirement as with the original specifications,* until we can stop.

First, we must reflect the additional information in the output. The addition of revised (scheduled) dates and dollars requires modifying the Monthly Project Status Report.

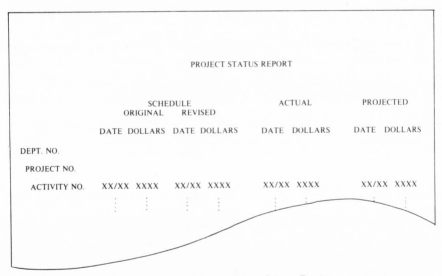

Figure 7.24. Revised Project Status Report.

What about the data base? Clearly, we need to modify the data base as well. To keep it simple, we'll just show the data by activity. (See Figure 7.25.)

The process of applying structured systems design is a systematic one. It is a method of working from outputs to inputs, from the known to derive the unknown. One of the principal advantages of this approach over many others is that there are fewer points from which you must start over. As in the example below, you have to make changes or start over every time some new output is required, or the manner of deriving output is changed. But changes are *designed into* the system. This represents a significant advantage in the development of correct, rational systems. Too often in the past, we have simply added new features onto an existing system without thinking through what impact those changes are likely to have on the system as a whole. As a result, we have introduced a great deal of redundancy (and error) into our systems and, at the same time, have made them nearly unintelligible.

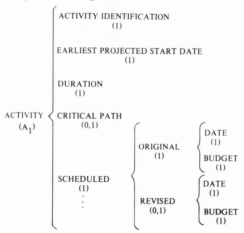

Figure 7.25. Data base diagram by activity.

In a structured systems design, each action has its own place(s), as does each piece of data. Each change in the output, in the way output is derived, or in the events reflected in the output causes a well-defined change in the systems design and/or the systems data base. The systems design directly reflects the requirements of the system. If it doesn't, we have a complex system and we know we are going to have extreme difficulty in making complex systems work.

The process of producing a correct systems design, given a clear understanding of the user's requirements, is a kind of giant logical puzzle. But it does have a solution. Structured systems design, structured data base design, and data structured programming are methods of arriving at well-defined logical solutions to complex systems problems.

Our systems description, if it is to be comprehensive, must provide the complete and exhaustive statement of each action and data element.

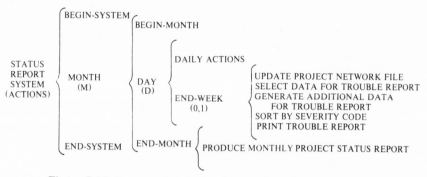

Figure 7.26. Systems description of actions and data elements.

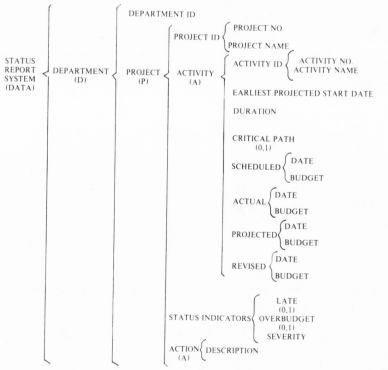

Figure 7.27. Complete systems description.

To restate the process of applying structured systems design, we can use a Warnier Diagram:

LOGICAL DESIGN CYCLE (C)

- USE WARNIER DIAGRAM TO STATE GENERAL PROBLEM
- IDENTIFY THE STRUCTURE (AND FREQUENCY) OF THE SYSTEMS OUTPUTS
- IDENTIFY THE LOGICAL DATA BASE OF THE SYSTEM
- PLACE THE SYSTEMS REQUIREMENTS INTO A BASIC SYSTEMS FLOW HIERARCHY
- LOOK TO SEE IF DATA REQUIRED ALREADY EXISTS
- IDENTIFY EVENTS IN REAL WORLD WHICH AFFECT THE DATA BASE
- PLACE LOGICAL UPDATING ACTIONS INTO BASIC SYSTEMS HIERARCHY

Figure 7.28. Warnier Diagram of the logical design process.

As you can see, we don't assume that we can go through the design process only once. The design cycle should be repeated for each new output, going only as far as you have to. Indeed, many traditional systems approaches fail simply because management assumes, wrongly, that one pass through the design approach will work. In fact, it rarely does work, and we should admit it.

Correctness in systems design

A few years ago, people began asking whether there was a way to prove that a program was correct. They recognized that testing could only show that no failures had been discovered, but not that the program was free of error, no matter how much testing was done. So a whole new school of addressing the problem of program correctness arose. Since most of the work in this area is highly mathematical, it is difficult for many people to follow. However, Warnier's logical data structured programming has made proving the correctness of even a relatively large program a practical matter.

We are now entering an era in which we will have to be able to prove the correctness of entire systems. This is especially true with respect to on-line, real-time systems that handle such life-and-death situations as air-traffic control, patient monitoring, or electronic funds transfer. Clearly, the proof of correctness of large systems is a major undertaking, a subject impossible to address in this book. However, a number of insights allow us to consider for the first time the meaning of the correctness of systems and of the data within the system.

As stated earlier, correct systems design involves getting the right sets of actions done on the right sets of data at the right time. Thus, if we can prove that we have a systems framework in which this must happen, then we will have achieved our basic objective. But what does this mean? If we have a correct logical expression of our problem, we can ensure that that description is carried throughout the system itself using the same tools at the systems level as are employed at the program level.

The entire structured revolution began, in part, as an outgrowth of many people attempting to establish the correctness of program designs. Over the last ten years, this approach has produced many interesting results. Curiously, the area which first attracted attention, i.e., the proof of mathematical and scientific programs, is not the one in which the greatest gains have been made. For a variety of reasons, scientific and mathematical programming proofs of correctness are hard to come by. However, for the bulk of our work (the development of business and commercial programs), Warnier's methodology, built upon the mathematical foundations of set theory, represents a remarkable breakthrough.

A few years ago, the mere idea of establishing the correctness of an entire system would have been unthinkable. Indeed, until quite recently, we did not even have a reasonable idea of how a correct system might look. By recognizing that a correct system is one in which the right sets of actions are done on the right sets of data at the right time, we are now in a position to look more seriously at what it might be like to develop a correct system. Indeed, we can see now that developing a correct system is largely a matter of the proper grouping (structuring) of sets of actions (programs, procedures) and sets of data (data bases, files, records) in such a way that we can assure that all of the logical requirements of the system are met.

For example, in the system we have been developing to produce project status information, we have been continuously concerned to make sure that each set of data and each set of actions which we have defined had a logical placement within the systems or data base framework. This insistence on correct grouping and ordering provides the proof of correctness that the system will do exactly what is required, and nothing else.

The emphasis upon logical correctness, coupled with the appropriate tools, has begun to yield significant results. One is the growing awareness that most systems in business applications fall into predictable patterns, based on time. In case after case, we find systems whose basic chart looks like the the one below:

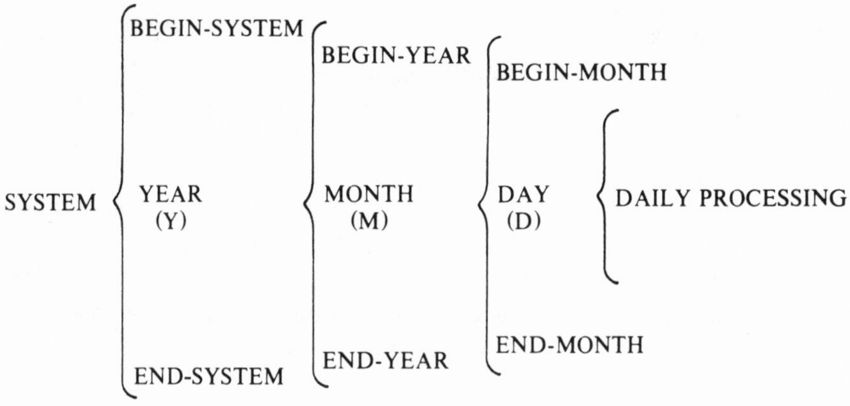

Figure 7.29. Basic systems chart.

Such a design, we find, is not accidental. Most business organizations manage a great many of their functions on a calendar basis. Moreover, even though the functions being managed may, in fact, be considerably different, they are often very similar in information systems operation.

Correctness, like so many other things, turns out to be quite simple to achieve, if you have designed it into the system. Moreover, solutions to other problems — such as how to logically fit a time frame that is not quite as nicely oriented as years, months, and weeks — also can be developed.

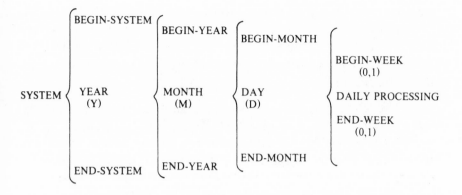

Figure 7.30. Systems functions organized on a calendar basis.

The logical placement of individual sets of actions, such as end-of-week and end-of-month operations, is an extremely critical one. Historically, in part because of our lack of tools and training, we have failed to design systems that include only enough detail to insure that just the logical activities that we required were built into our systems in exactly the correct places. Structured systems design can now assure us that our systems will work as required before we put them on the machine.

It may seem that the approach we are describing here is an overly mechanical one. Often, systems analysts suggest that they do not want to be as specific as structured systems design requires, because they want to allow flexibility. Unfortunately, what they provide is flexibility to be wrong. Such flexibility is no great service to anyone, especially the user. Increasingly, structured systems designs are working better and more reliably because the analyst has carefully laid out each set of operations so that the correct ones must be done in the correct order. The impact of such a small change is enormous.

In building a structured system, we have not eliminated the necessity to do thorough analysis. Nor have we come up with any foolproof methodology. We are reaching the point, however, when it will be possible to deliver to our users exactly what they asked for. That alone represents a major break with the past. If the user asks for the wrong things, then we will unfortunately provide him with the wrong things. But at least we can defend what we did; and moreover, we can feel confident that if the right things can be specified, we can provide them in a reasonable time frame.

The correctness of a systems design, as we have said before, is the minimum that a systems analyst can deliver. If we cannot guarantee the validity of the results that our systems produce, then we have violated our professional ethics. Structured systems design will not provide miracle solutions. In fact, our solutions, in many cases, look remarkably like the good solutions of earlier eras. However, we are now in the position of being able to better understand and deal with our new solutions, and to maintain them at a far lower cost.

If we can show that the Warnier Diagram above (Figure 7.30) has been implemented (i.e., if we test the system logically), and if we can show that only the right sets of data are ever accessed, then we can be confident that the output produced by MONTH-END PROCESSING or QUARTER-END PROCESSING, and so forth, will be correct. Moreover, this will be true of any set of information with which we are apt to deal.

Correctness in systems design is actually no more difficult (or no easier) to determine than is correctness of a complex or a simple program. The problem is fundamentally a logical, not a computer, one. Correct systems, then, depend upon correct programs and correct data. If we can show that the correct sets of actions always are done on the correct sets of data at the correct times within our systems designs, we also will know that our system is correct. We are only part way there. Correctness of output depends upon the correctness (or integrity) of the data base used; and that leads to a second major logical part to structuring systems, *the structuring of data.*

8 OTHER STRUCTURED DESIGN TOOLS

During the past few years, due largely to the excitement over structured programming, quite a number of tools for documenting structured systems designs other than Warnier Diagrams have been developed to assist the systems analyst do a better, more professional job. All of the tools discussed in this section were first developed more or less as structured programming aids and then adapted to fit systems design as well. While I feel that Warnier Diagrams generally do a better overall job as a universal design tool, each of these other tools is valuable in its own way for communicating certain types of problems for certain audiences.

Structured narratives

The first truly structured design tool that I myself used was something I like to call a "structured narrative." The use of structured narratives was a direct outgrowth of examples I had seen of pseudocode or pidgin language used by IBM and others to sketch their structured programming solutions. (IBM called it PDL for Program Design Language.)

The use of pseudolanguages is probably as old as programming itself. In fact, I remember dimly the very first good programmer I ever met had a shorthand method of putting his thoughts in a form that wasn't quite English and wasn't quite a recognizable programming language either (quasi-ALGOL he used to call it). Indeed, people often need some informal means of writing down the logical structure of a problem without enforcing the rigor required when actually writing code that will be executed by a computer.

At any rate, the first attempts I made at structuring a program took shape in my own shorthand language somewhat before we had developed a good approach for doing structured programming in COBOL. To understand just how the structured programming solutions to certain problems would look, I needed to use a structured form of English.

As we experimented with the structured narrative as a means of expression, I became convinced that not only was it possible to develop cleaner solutions to systems than possibly using other available techniques, but that these solutions also communicated better to all those involved in the systems process. In particular, we could develop a simple document that eliminated a great deal of confusion in the documentation of systems requirements.

You might care to experiment for yourself. First, study Figure 8.1. Then, turn the page and look at Figure 8.2. Now, ask yourself, suppose you were working to meet a strict deadline, which of the definitions would you prefer? Our experience has been nearly universal — a vast majority prefer the structured version of Figure 8.2 over the standard English shown in Figure 8.1. Indeed, as much as I love the English language, I am completely convinced that it is a poor vehicle for communicating complex logical ideas. *The use of structured narratives makes logic visible,* as do all structured methods of documentation currently used.

We have increasingly used structured narratives over the past few years and have found it necessary to develop a formal definition for the basic language constructs that matched those of logical structuring, namely functional references, alternation, repetition, and sequence. In time, we coined the term Systems Design Language (SDL) to describe what we had done and, at the same time, to remove the stigma of its programming origins.

Certainly, SDL is by no means an original invention. Indeed, we find that more and more people are inventing their own form of structured narrative all the time. But since all of these languages accomplish the same basic result, they are fundamentally compatible.

SEPARATION PROCESSING AS IT AFFECTS POSITION DATA

MAJOR FUNCTIONS PERFORMED

1. To remove an employee from the position now filled by him on the Personnel Position File through CRT terminals.

INPUTS TO PROGRAM

1. Information entered through terminal from the Change of Employee Status Form (DA-202).

2. The on-line Position File.

OUTPUTS OF PROGRAM

1. Terminal display of Position File information.

2. The on-line Position File with the separation processed.

3. A Separation Record generated to a file to be printed in the Appointments and Separations Reports at a later time.

4. Transactions generated for backup purposes.

VALIDATION AND EDIT CRITERIA

1. The AGENCY, DEPARTMENT, POSITION NUMBER, and SOCIAL SECURITY NUMBER of the Separation Transaction must match those fields in the Position Record before processing.

ACTION TO BE TAKEN ON ERROR OR EXCEPTION CONDITIONS

1. If any information being entered does not pass the edit routines, a message will appear, and that information must be reentered. It will again be edited.

2. If any error occurs and the correct data are unavailable to the operator, the original Position Record remains unchanged on the file and this one separation cannot be processed until corrected.

LOGICAL RULES AND DECISIONS

1. Move the entered DATE-VACATED to the incumbent DATE-VACATED.

2. Check NOTIFY-WHEN-VACANT field, and display or print an appropriate message for the operator identified there.

3. Save TRANSACTION NUMBER and all information on backup file.

Figure 8.1. Standard English version of problem solution.

SEPARATION PROCESSING AS IT AFFECTS POSITION DATA

```
GET TRANSACTION DATA.
GET POSITION RECORD.
IF NO SUCH POSITION
  THEN
    DISPLAY 'NO SUCH POSITION.'
  ELSE
    EDIT TRANSACTION DATA.
    IF ERROR IN TRANSACTION
      THEN
        DISPLAY ERRORS.
      ELSE
        IF NOTIFY-WHEN-VACANT
          THEN
            DISPLAY NOTIFICATION MESSAGE.
          ELSE
            NEXT SENTENCE.
        END-IF
        MOVE DATE-VACATED TO INCUMBENT DATE-VACATED.
        UPDATE POSITION FILE.
        SAVE TRANSACTION ON BACKUP FILE.
    END-IF
END-IF
```

Figure 8.2. Structured narrative of same solution.

For a more complete definition of SDL, see Appendix A; but let us look now at a couple of uses of SDL on problems already discussed:

```
DO FOR EACH HOSPITAL;
      DO FOR EACH PATIENT;
        IF PATIENT IS ACTIVE
          THEN
            COMPUTE AND PRINT BILL;
          ELSE
            SKIP;
        END-IF;
      END-DO;              or, alternatively
END-DO;
                            FOR EACH HOSPITAL;
                              FOR EACH PATIENT;
                                WHEN PATIENT IS ACTIVE;
                                  COMPUTE AND PRINT BILL;
                                OTHERWISE,
                                  SKIP;
```

Once you become completely proficient with any form of structuring, the ability to switch back and forth from one to the other becomes natural. Since we find that certain audiences prefer one method of documentation over another, the ability to relate your ideas in different ways is a plus.

Structured narratives have been a principal tool for documenting complex logical problems for some time now. In many installations, SDL (or something similar) is used as a formal means to improve communications. In fact, I recently saw an example of a structured narrative included in a proposal that an internal service bureau had prepared for one of its clients.

The reason structured narratives are so successful is that they deal with complex situations in a direct understandable fashion. While many people insist on unstructured English narratives to document systems requirements for users, we find that in most cases natural languages, such as English, obscure logical problems rather than make them clear. Indeed, the ambiguity that results from unstructured communications creates tremendous problems later in systems development.

One day after I had presented one of my standard lectures on the value of structured documentation, one of my students, who was a manager, stated that, notwithstanding all the things I had said, his installation found that certain things could only be documented in standard English. He gave the following example, which I have modified slightly to protect the source:

If the group code is zero, then parameters 2, 3, 4, and 5 on this record are used for all groups in this run. If the group code is not zero but the last two positions XXOO are zero, then parameters 6 through 12 of this record are used for all groups with the same two nonzero digits. If the group code is not zero nor are the last two positions zero, then the parameters of this record are used only for this group.

Get that? Well, if you didn't, you're not alone. Using this example in class usually evokes gales of laughter. What's funny, I find, is not that this is a particularly poor piece of writing (it isn't), but it's that such documentation is altogether too familiar for most of my students. As a matter of fact, I've had some people say that compared to the specifications they were used to receiving, the example was very clear. As an exercise, the reader should develop a structured narrative of the problem for himself.

Communication is a difficult business, but often it's regarded far too lightly. For the most part, we are not taught good writing habits in school; and typically not until we have to write something that counts in business or in the professional world do we understand exactly how unprepared we are to communicate.

Another problem, though, is that unstructured English, or any other natural language, is simply not a good mechanism for expressing complex logical thoughts. No amount of playing with the language will correct that problem. Indeed, one of the major faults of certain computer programming languages, especially COBOL, is that they try to look like unstructured English. Only after we began to take complex problems and structure did we understand why we were making so many slips between the user and the computer.

Too often, when unstructured documentation techniques are used to document user requirements, a good many of those requirements never are translated into the operating programs. A study some years ago showed that a large portion of an average programmer's time is spent doing things that could best be called "systems queries," that is, things the analyst had gotten wrong, overlooked, or failed to communicate to the programmer. A common experience in the systems business is that something always falls between the cracks. From the user to the analyst, to the programmer, and to the computer, something is forever getting misplaced, misquoted, or omitted. All structured documentation techniques alleviate this problem of communication.

Other examples of SDL are:

```
MONTHLY SYSTEM:

BEGIN;
    DO FOR EACH MONTH
      DO UNTIL NO ERROR
        RUN EDIT ROUTINE;
      IF ERROR
        THEN
          FIND AND CORRECT ERROR;
        ELSE
          SKIP;
      END-IF
      END-DO (EDIT CYCLE);
      UPDATE MASTER FILE;
      PRODUCE MONTHLY STATISTICAL REPORT;
    END-DO (MONTH);
END;
```

```
CASE
        IF TYPE = A/R  DO A/R PROCESSING;
      ELSE IF TYPE = ORDER  DO ORDER PROCESSING;
      ELSE IF TYPE = NAME CHANGE  DO NAME CHANGE;
          ELSE DO ERROR -1- PROCESS;
END-CASE
```

Structured box diagrams (Nassi-Shneiderman Charts)

Another method of developing a structured narrative is something we'll call a "structured box diagram." The structured box diagram combines a structured narrative with a graphic means of showing a series of Chinese boxes, each piece nested within the other to show the important logical relations. These charts are known by a number of names, the rightful name probably being Nassi-Shneiderman Charts after their inventors. The following is one example:

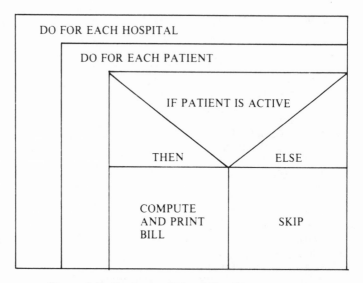

Figure 8.3. Example of Nassi-Shneiderman Chart.

To many people, these charts give an overall feeling for the nesting of one logical function within another. From a design standpoint, structured box diagrams are often difficult to expand, since it is necessary to continually redraw the diagram as you proceed deeper into the structure of the problem. Another form of the same idea is shown below:

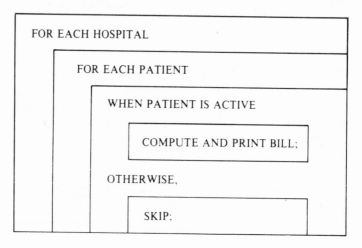

Figure 8.4. Alternative version of same chart.

And here's still another example just to show that it is basically a mechanical task to convert a Warnier Diagram into a structured box diagram:

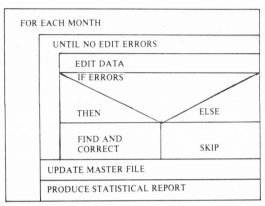

Figure 8.5. Another example of a structured box diagram.

Ultimately, structured box diagrams simply draw lines around the indented portions of a structured narrative to emphasize the logical nesting. In some cases, it improves the readability, while in others it does little or nothing. One negative feature noticed in using both the structured narratives and structured box diagrams is the tendency to obscure the logical hierarchy. Since logical, data-related hierarchies are major tools in structured design, we see this tendency as a serious drawback of both techniques.

Structured flowcharts

Since structuring is simply a method of logical organization, structuring is readily applicable to existing techniques for documenting systems and programs, especially flowcharts. Sometimes, it is useful to be able to convert a Warnier Diagram or other structured documents into a flowchart. This is particularly important when working with a computer language like FORTRAN or assembler that requires implementation of a structured solution using conditional and unconditional branches. For example, the following Warnier Diagram (Figure 8.6) is converted into the structured flowchart in Figure 8.7:

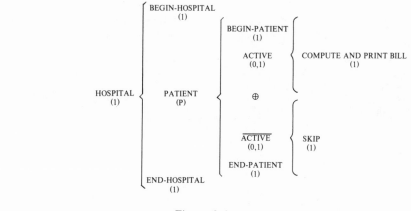

Figure 8.6. Warnier Diagram.

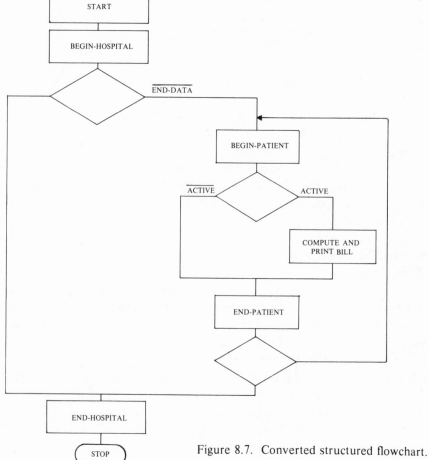

Figure 8.7. Converted structured flowchart.

There always is, in fact, a simple method of flowcharting a Warnier Diagram, no matter how complex the problem. Moreover, each flowchart can fit on a single page, so that all references to details of the process are by named module. In the above case, the various modules, BEGIN-HOSPITAL, BEGIN-PATIENT, COMPUTE AND PRINT BILL, and so on, are all treated as modules, each with its own structured flowchart.

The rules for structured flowcharting, once recognized, are simple to apply:

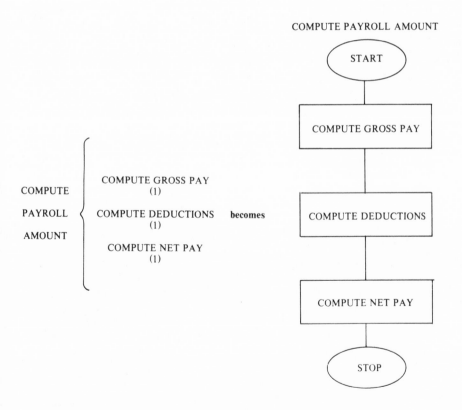

Figure 8.8. Sequence structured flowchart.

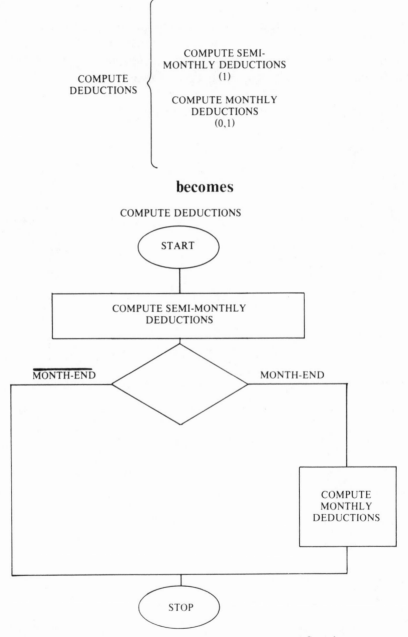

Figure 8.9. Sequence and alternation structured flowchart.

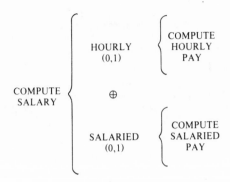

becomes

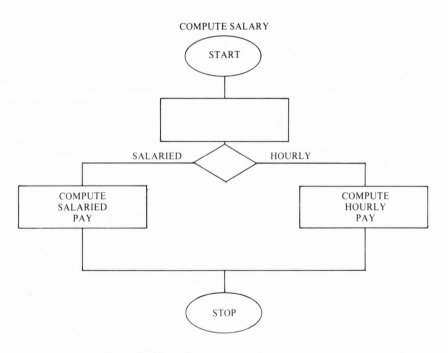

Figure 8.10. Alternation structured flowchart.

The only peculiar rule to observe is that repetition must be flowcharted as a post-test (DO UNTIL) loop. Thus,

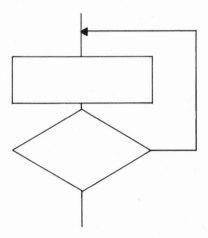

Figure 8.11. Repetition (DO UNTIL) structured flowchart.

This constraint really poses no problem, for to develop a well-structured pretest loop (DO WHILE), just add a single test before entering a loop, like so:

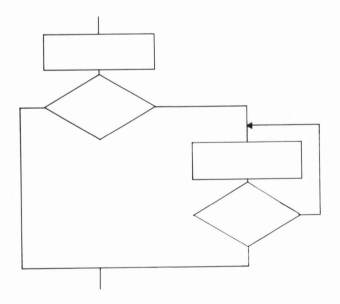

Figure 8.12. Repetition (DO WHILE or PERFORM UNTIL)
structured flowchart.

This method produces good-looking flowcharts, and, indeed, the first thing I noticed about Warnier's work was the neat appearance of his flowcharts. I knew he simply had to be doing structured programming, no matter what he called it. It is sometimes easy to miss such an obvious convention. For example, recently reviewing a book on structured programming in COBOL, I found a flowchart of the following form:

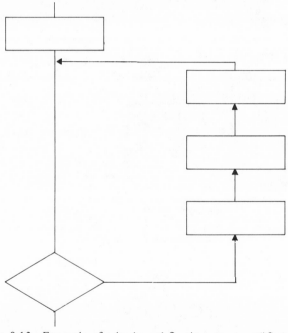

Figure 8.13. Example of a backward-flowing structured flowchart.

At any rate, our final hospital-patient program as shown in Figure 8.14 looks just as good in structured flowchart form as it did as a Warnier Diagram.

Structured flowcharts are particularly useful in communicating with unreconstructed programmers like myself. Sometimes I tell people that I don't care how they code the problem, so long as they let me draw the flowchart, and they follow the chart exactly — so much for GOTO-less programming. Who cares about coding, so long as the approach to designing a problem is structured.

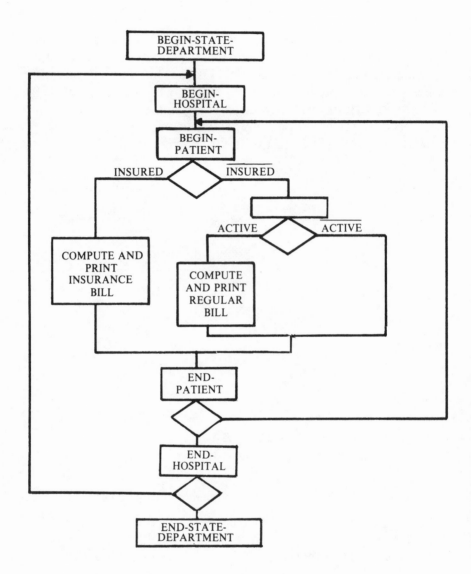

Figure 8.14. Flowchart of hospital program example.

A number of this section's reviewers have taken issue with my comments about flowcharting loops. Generally, they say, often strongly, that obviously one ought to test at the top of a loop in order to avoid the problem of a loop with no occurrences.

They point correctly to all the trouble FORTRAN has caused over the years with its post-test loops. And after all, they add, one way is just as good as another.

How to reply? Certainly, a number of equivalent ways represent the same logical condition, but there are several reasons for choosing one method of representation over another. For example, the logical idea we are attempting to represent is a logical construct — repetition (not the DO WHILE statement, although this is one way to implement repetition). Clearly, then, we can use the following diagram to represent a logical condition in which some function "x" is done 1 to n times.

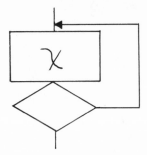

Figure 8.15. Flowchart of a logical condition.

But what about a loop which occurs 0 to n times? Flowchart it as two logical entities:

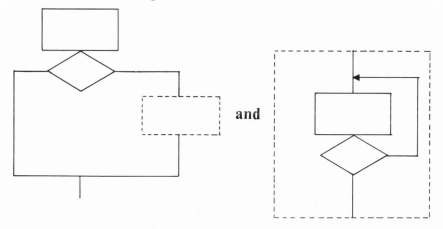

Figure 8.16. Flowcharts of looping logical conditions.

Much discussion in the last few years has been devoted to the effect that structured coding has upon improving comprehension. One of the major improvements is that structured programs read from top to bottom. Following the logical flow of the code of a structured program, the eye (and, therefore, the mind) needs only to proceed in one direction. The only time the eye needs to go upward is to repeat a section. Consider the following charts:

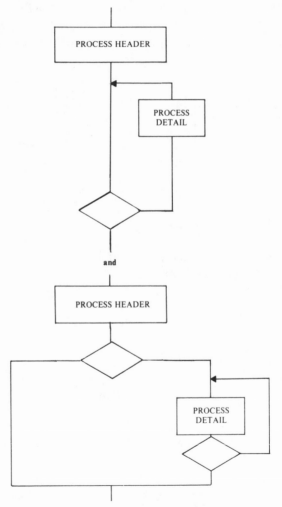

Figure 8.17. Charts with same end result but different structures.

Both charts perform the same function, but one proceeds top to bottom while the other does not. In addition, one cannot add detail to the chart on the top without also adding considerable confusion. Suppose we wished to expand the logic for processing a detail into alternative processing for orders and accounts receivable records. The chart below (a) is less clear than the chart (b) that follows it:

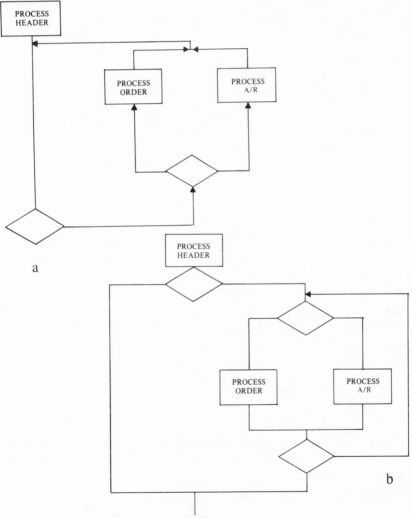

Figure 8.18. Flowcharts for alternative processing.

Of course, the problem worsens as the top-down development of the problem expands.

At its root, the problem of deciding at which end of a loop to place a test (a pretest or post-test loop) is not a quarrel over which is better, since we can always restate one in terms of the other with the help of alternation. The problem rather is how to represent repetition using structured flowcharts. For reasons of clarity, then, we choose to show a pretest loop as an initial logical alternation followed by a post-test.

The additional test, though it works, seems uneconomical and redundant to many structured programmers. However, the price is a small one to pay when considering the improvement in comprehension as well as in the ability to map any other form of structured representation, such as Warnier Diagrams, Nassi-Shneiderman Charts, or pseudocode into a flowchart that reads top to bottom. Redundancy is the price paid for logical consistency.

Like reading data at the top of a loop, testing at the top is intuitively appealing, especially considering the problems caused for years by executing a loop once, even when there is no data. However, making the test twice now seems altogether reasonable from all standpoints possible: efficiency, correctness, and ease of understanding. On my office wall is a quote from B. Kernighan and P.J. Plauger's *Elements of Programming Style,* which states a loop ought "to do nothing gracefully."[1] I agree completely with the spirit of this comment. For example, take the flowchart in Figure 8.19.

When I use that chart as a logical way to process data, I am often asked, "But what do you do if there are no records on the file?" I reply, "I make sure that I don't call this program!" Indeed, unless you simply enjoy watching the operating system grind away, I can't think of any good reason for executing a program with no data.

---

[1]B. Kernighan and P.J. Plauger. *The Elements of Programming Style.* (New York: McGraw Hill, 1974), p. 88.

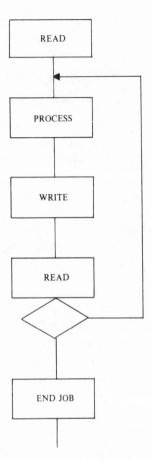

Figure 8.19. Flowchart with a post-test loop.

The pretest loop is not the universal answer to all our programming problems. Like so many things, the failure to process
a loop correctly is usually the symptom of some deeper logical
malady. We can treat the problem by making all loops pretest
loops, but that is somewhat akin to treating with aspirin a fever
caused by an infection. The fever may go away for a while; but
unless we treat the underlying infection, the fever will come
back. Similarly, if we don't understand that a set of actions that
must be done 0 to n times is different from one that must be
done 1 to n times, we will be hard pressed to make our problems

go away forever. In fact, we will simply move them around. As in so many cases, Warnier has worked out this problem rather well. As mentioned before, it was his flowcharts, not his prose, that convinced me he was doing truly structured programming.

HIPO/DB diagrams

If you've been around data processing for a while and consequently have read the literature, you probably have been exposed to a technique that is often used in conjunction with structured programming and structured design, called Hierarchical-Input-Process-Output (HIPO) charts. As far as I can tell, HIPO charts were not originally developed as a design tool but rather as a documentation aid. The technique was developed and refined within IBM partly in response to a need for a wiring diagram for programs.

A typical HIPO package can be broken into three major parts: (1) the visual table of contents (Figure 8.20), (2) the overview IPO diagram (Figure 8.21), and (3) the detailed IPO diagram (Figure 8.22). With these charts, it was thought possible to portray a software product as completely as a well-engineered piece of electronics and, in the absence of alternatives, the HIPO methodology certainly is much better than nothing at all.

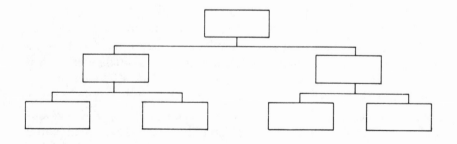

Figure 8.20. Visual table of contents of HIPO package.

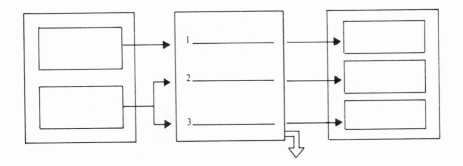

Figure 8.21. Overview IPO diagram.

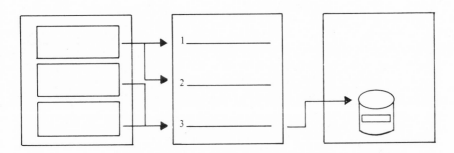

Figure 8.22. Detailed IPO diagram.

By looking at the three diagrams, one can see how the HIPO package shows the basic systems or program hierarchy and the relationship between program and data, all of which are particularly important to systems design.

From a structured systems design standpoint, however, HIPO has a number of deficiencies, the first being that it is not structured. Thinking of our previous discussion of analysis, you will see that HIPO is primarily an analytical model. HIPO provides a better-than-average tool for breaking down problems in a strictly hierarchical manner, but with no deep concern for how the pieces fit together at the end. For example, the following IPO might be a representation of the first analytical model that we developed:

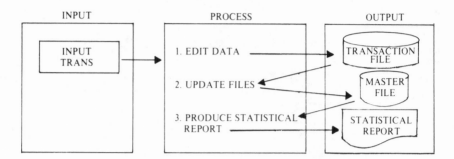

Figure 8.23. IPO model of original example.

The second solution might look as follows:

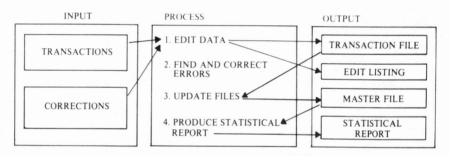

Figure 8.24. IPO version of second solution.

This is certainly not a structured solution, because we don't know precisely the fashion in which each part of the system fits together. Unfortunately, since HIPO was originally designed as a documentation tool, it does not require each module to fit together in a structured fashion to improve the logical design.

Many users of HIPO have found to their dismay that a considerable amount of work remained if they were to develop a well-structured program from a set of complete HIPO documents. This is not a fatal problem, however, because it is possible to structure a standard HIPO chart quite easily by replacing the process box of the IPO chart with a structured narrative or structured box diagram, as demonstrated on the facing page in Figure 8.25:

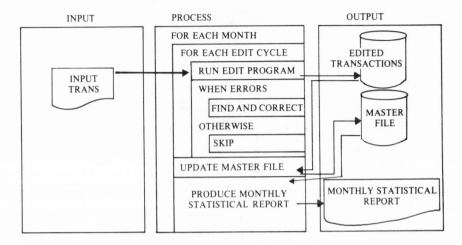

Figure 8.25. Structured IPO chart.

Observing the IPO diagrams developed, you will find a curious thing: There are arrows from the output block to the process block. What could that mean? Some of the data for Step 4, for example, is output from a previous step in the same process. This flow of data from right to left as well as from left to right is a manifestation of a serious lack in a HIPO package: the failure to distinguish between systems requirements and systems architecture.

Earlier, in the chapter on our basic systems model, we began to identify a set of data — called the data base — that remained within the black box. That particular set of data was a fundamental part of the systems architecture. In a system, we needed some way to distinguish between internal and external sets of data. From our standpoint, then, the most serious fault of HIPO is its lack of the concept of a logical systems data base in which various data are stored for future use.

The solution I came up with, following Warnier, was to introduce a slightly different form with an additional box into the HIPO model. The box is labeled DATA BASE.

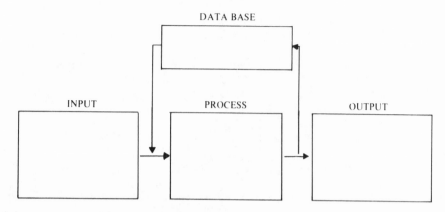

Figure 8.26. HIPO model with DATA BASE box.

By making this modification, we are able to work the
HIPO/DB (HIPO/DATA BASE) model into our concept of
structured systems design, while preserving the structured systems design philosophy. Now, it is possible to refer unambigu-
ously to our original systems model.

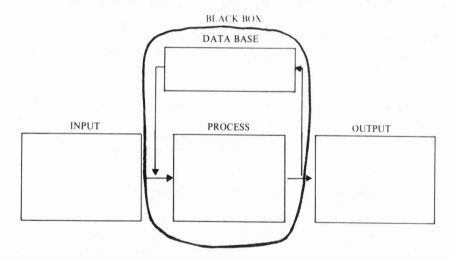

Figure 8.27. HIPO/DB model.

Indeed, we also are able to identify clearly for the first time
which elements relate to systems requirements and which to systems architecture. For example:

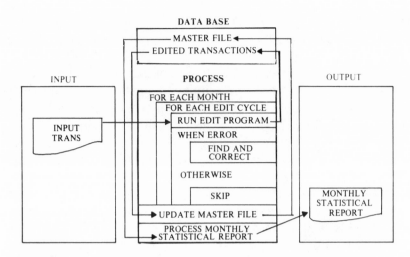

Figure 8.28. Identified elements of systems requirements and architecture.

A footnote on structured documentation tools

By systematically structuring problems, we can help pro-grammers, analysts, and managers begin to understand which data are needed for their own sake, and which data are needed to produce something else. In general, the use of HIPO/DB in con-junction with SDL represented a major milestone in the develop-ment of a sound and logically consistent structured approach. For one thing, it integrated the ideas of hierarchical design, structured programming, and data base design into a single model. Moreover, as a result of the structuring, people under-stood these diagrams extremely. well.

However, a couple of significant problems remained in the use of HIPO/DB as a design tool. One was that it often took a great deal of time to construct and to maintain a HIPO/DB di-agram. But yet a larger problem was that there were simply too many of them. HIPO's major deficiency then lies in the amount of documentation required initially and later. In using these techniques, we shifted our attention in many cases from the solution of the problem to keeping track of all the documentation in the system. For small problems, this was not of major significance; however, for large systems, the volume of HIPO documentation easily gets out of hand.

To make a long story short, we found that the function of the HIPO/DB charts could be eliminated in favor of using Warnier Diagrams throughout. This has had a major impact on both the quantity and quality of the systems documentation, because HIPO/DB, like HIPO, resurrects the old forest-and-tree problem: By having to deal with too many documents, we became concerned about trees and bark, but had an increasingly difficult time locating the forest.

In summary, there are a number of good structured documentation techniques: Warnier Diagrams, structured narratives, structured block diagrams, structured flowcharts, and HIPO/DB, to name a few. Over time, we have gravitated, along with our clients, to the use of the modified Warnier Diagram as our principal tool, because it seems to communicate better to more people in the shortest amount of time. Each of these structured tools has its place, and the best method depends upon the audience being addressed. But remember that any tool can be abused. In general, I like Warnier Diagrams and dislike the basic HIPO forms, but I've seen some terrible Warnier Diagrams and some very good HIPO charts. On the other hand, the various techniques are not all equal. The basic Warnier Diagram is the fastest, easiest, and best communicating device we've ever employed, and those who have tried it seem to agree.

The reason we present more than one method of structured documentation is so that you will be able to make an easy mental translation whenever you are in a foreign technical land where the native tongue is HIPO, pseudocode, structured block diagrams, or flowcharts. One good rule of thumb — if someone shows you documentation that purports to describe something in a structured way, try to produce a Warnier Diagram or structured narrative quickly without any further explanation. If you can't, you can bet that the documentation is not structured.

Relationship of structured systems design
to other structured techniques

Throughout this book, we have used the terms structured, logical, and hierarchical to describe our approach. We also have discussed Warnier's work in glowing terms. However, it is very important to underscore the differences between structured systems design as I conceive it and other approaches, in particular Jean-Dominique Warnier's L.C.P./L.C.S. (Logical Construction of Programs/Logical Construction of Systems) techniques.

The most important difference between our techniques from the beginning is that we have chosen to apply the basic knowledge of logical structuring to an entire system, instead of to segments of a process, and to undefined as well as to defined problems. In general, most of the systems approaches we've examined attack only a small part of the systems problem, such as producing a correct program from a given set of specifications. However, there is little actual application of these tools to systems problem solving in the real world.

In a manner of speaking, structured systems design is a synthesis of a number of techniques, including traditional systems design, structured programming, Warnier's L.C.P., data base theory, and symbolic logic. We have not only adopted some of Warnier's method of diagramming, but we have adapted it for documenting complex logical problems wherever we find them, something which Warnier himself does not yet do.

In one sense, structured systems design takes advantage of the best of all possible worlds, since we have coupled logical, data structured analysis (from L.C.P.) with structured programming and data base management. By doing so, we have eliminated many problems of translation of logical statements to programs. In many cases, we simply program from the Warnier Diagram. As more and more is learned about structured systems development, we expect to see automated tools evolve that will capitalize on the logical output-oriented philosophy represented here.

The last few years represent a period of extensive adaptation and modification of many of the theories of systems design and analysis. Certain of these ideas have proved unworkable or to be merely a by-product of other concepts. For example, the concept of good modularity that has played such a large part in the programming literature recently has turned out to be a by-product, not a major goal, of a good systems design process.

Warnier Diagrams are a way of looking at problems in a new fashion. (I chose to call them Warnier Diagrams; but whether you call them Warnier-Orr Diagrams or expansion diagrams, they are an important mind-expanding discovery, a link between logic, problem solving, and human communication.) Structured systems design has profited greatly by using such tools in conjunction with an age-old philosophical approach called teleology (the study of goals) to arrive at our output-oriented approach.

No one can forecast where the field of systems building (or informatics) will lead us. In the relatively short span of ten years, we have made remarkable progress to the point where we can now begin to talk about a system as a whole, rather than as simply a collection of parts.

9 BRIDGING THE APPLICATIONS GAP

When a new technology is introduced, it always takes time for that information to be assimilated into daily business. This is particularly true when the change is a basic theoretical one. Structured systems development is just such a case. The approach itself is absolutely independent of computer languages or any exotic kind of electronics, and yet, it represents a major breakthrough in problem solving because it is a new way of thinking about problems.

In the last few chapters, we have introduced a number of new approaches and tools, all aimed primarily at helping the systems professional to:

- find problems
- understand problems
- solve problems, and
- communicate with people who have problems

But it is a far cry from understanding a tool or a methodology and being able to apply it, for application requires that you not only understand how to use a tool but also that you understand when to use it and on what subject.

So far, we've developed a conceptual model for systems design and explained some of the fundamental tools employed. However, a master craftsman is not characterized so much by having the right tools as he is by the way in which he uses those tools. Anyone can buy the right set of tools or acquire a good education, but it is something else to be able to create a quality product with them.

In the information systems business, a quality product is one that solves an information handling problem in a correct, economical, and manageable manner; moreover, it should not be any more sophisticated than what the problem calls for.

Let's use an analogy. An architect has a great many tools with which to work, and each day science gives him new ones. On the other hand, most of the basics of engineering and design are the same as they were years ago. The average architect spends much of his life learning not only to use certain tools and approaches, but also how and when to do so. Few architects, even with interactive graphics, can produce a fraction of the quality of a Frank Lloyd Wright.

In our analogy, the systems analyst can be compared directly to the architect, and the various logical tools we discussed so far can be thought of as the design instruments. We have now reached a point in our learning where we are ready to look at ways to apply these tools, ways which correspond roughly to the architect's design approach. This is terribly important, for in systems development, as in architecture, the order of implementation makes a great deal of difference. And we must not confuse the order of thinking about a problem with the order of execution. For example, in constructing a building, we begin with the foundation. But in designing a building, we cannot design the foundation until we first know how big the building will be and how much weight the foundation must support at various places — the foundation is, in fact, the last thing we design.

Compare this to developing a system. If we are constructing a system that produces monthly reports, we need to install the basic data base before we can produce the reports. On the other hand, as stated earlier, we start by designing the output reports and working backward to determine what data we need to collect and how and when to do so. This is relatively easy to do in a small system, and becomes progressively harder as the system grows. However, the bigger the system, the more important is the design.

So, how do you do structured systems design? I've already given you a number of clues, e.g., "start with the output and work backward," "concentrate on the logical structure," and so on. These are great for your bulletin board, but how do you use those clues to design a system from scratch, or, more likely, to make changes in a large unstructured system that already exists? Some of the details will be discussed in the next two books in this series: *Structuring Data* and *Data Structured Programming.* Before we conclude this book, we need to investigate the order of structuring a system.

Prior to discussing how to do things right, let's look at how to do them wrong. The following sequence of activities is drawn from a number of sources, all firsthand, including my own experiences. It might be called the "log of the Project Titanic."

Step 1: Select Due Date
Step 2: Select Acronym (optional)
Step 3: Select Turkey (i.e., project manager)
Step 4: Develop Project Schedule
Step 5: Hire Systems Analysts
Step 6: Develop Systems Document
Step 7: Develop Input Specifications and Order Forms
Step 8: Hire Programmers
Step 9: Begin Work on Edit Program
Step 10: Begin Work on Conversion Programs
Step 11: Begin Design of Data Files
Step 12: Begin Work on Update Programs
Step 13: Hire More Programmers
Step 14: Begin Work on Output Reports, Screens, etc.
Step 15: Slip Schedule
Step 16: Hire More Programmers
Step 17: Panic
Step 18: Search for Guilty
Step 19: Punish Innocent
Step 20: Promote Uninvolved
Step 21: Go to Step 1

The steps above, unfortunately, are a more or less accurate history of any number of less than successful projects. I remember once asking a fellow who had been involved in some very large projects why they had failed to meet their objectives so often. His reply was: "Anyone with any smarts who had been on one large project will make damn sure he (or she) is never on another one. So on most large projects, you have either trainees or masochists!" Having been on a couple of large projects, I'm not quite sure how to react to that; but down deep, I know he's pretty close to being right.

There's no way to avoid large-scale projects, though. Somehow, through the use of better tools, better management, or better something, we simply have to produce better products than in the past.

I suppose I first recognized the self-destructive nature of the Project Titanic schedule at least eight or ten years ago. Why does it keep reoccurring? I could find no satisfactory answer until only quite recently. Now, the reasons for doing the right things in the wrong order seem particularly obvious. The problem had to do with the manner in which the project was conceived in the first place.

Let's go back to Step 1 in the Project Titanic schedule: Assign due date. You may laugh, but in far too many cases of systems failure, the due date is one of the first things established, before the project manager even knows whether he will build a system with ten programs or a hundred. Then, as early as Step 4 a project schedule is developed, again, in almost complete ignorance. Only one thing is known for sure at this point — the due date. Let's think about how the project schedule is likely to be decided, given a fixed due date.

Since we know when we have to be finished, we will probably work backward to develop a schedule that, on paper at any rate, will produce the desired system by the due date. We know that the last thing we need working is the part of the system that produces the output; and for that process, you must have a data base installed. Before that you must install the edit and update programs, and to have anything to process, you need to have input forms. But to have input forms delivered in time, you must have designed them yesterday, since by working backward you usually pass today's date. In fact, you usually come up with a chart that looks like the one below:

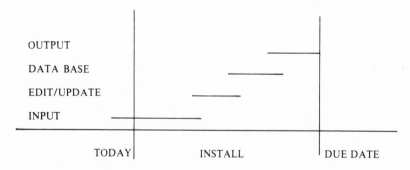

Figure 9.1. Project schedule developed by working backward.

Therefore, having committed to a due date before we knew what the problem really was, we suffer the results. If we think about it for a minute, our earlier analogy of the architect and the builder probably is appropriate. In general, a schedule such as the one above would be appropriate for constructing a new building, if the plans are already complete.

However, as a design and build philosophy, it is a disaster. We need to ask, what sequence would we like to design things, given a choice? The answer is: *in exactly the opposite order from installation*. While we would like to install a system in the order of execution, i.e., from input to output, we want to design a system from output to input, so that our schedule begins to look like the following:

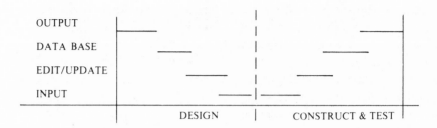

Figure 9.2. Project schedule of design of output to input.

This schedule says we had better design before we build. Moreover, it explains why the schedule of Project Titanic had so many backward loops. They resulted from making guesses early in a project and then discovering the guesses were wrong. By taking the design, construct, and test approach we avoid as many guesses as possible.

In general, the structured systems life cycle places far more importance on knowing what you are going to do before you make commitments.

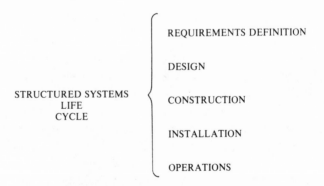

Figure 9.3. Structured systems life cycle.

As shown in the figure above, you cannot make any commitments about the completion of the project until you have a definition of the requirements. (Too often, we live to regret those hasty commitments.) Remember the rule: Design first. Although this rule is not easy to follow, especially when everyone else is panic-stricken, it is by far the best course and is always cheaper in the end. For this reason, the structured project approach is much more likely to lead to successful completion.

AFTERWORD

This book has only barely touched on a whole new technology related to doing systems. Even in the relatively short time involved in committing it to paper, I discovered a number of things that made the approach work better. What we are teaching here is by no means foolproof, nor is the technique polished. Each day, we learn things not known before, and even if we are eager, we absorb change very slowly.

It is ironic that the publisher of this book should be YOURDON inc. For years, I felt the approaches that I had developed were considerably different from (as well as better than) those of Larry Constantine and Ed Yourdon. I still feel that way. However, perhaps because I now understand their methods better, or because they have begun to change in order to deal with the kind of systems problems in which we were interested, we seem to have come closer together in our thinking. Today, while we are not in complete agreement, certainly not about such things as modularity and defensive programming, we are learning more and more about how our technologies fit together. This is possible only after admitting that you don't have all the answers.

When the historians of systems technology consider developments of the 1970's, they will likely find it to be one of the most explosive and creative periods ever. Having made a few key discoveries, we can look forward to a period of amazing productivity as information scientists work out the implications of these discoveries. Armed with a strong theory, we have a dramatic opportunity to increase our understanding of such things as systems.

Reading it now, I can see many faults in the book from a technical and, certainly, from a literary standpoint. Because we live in an age of great change, it seems to me to be far more important at this stage to expose my ideas to a larger public and let people criticize and comment on them. I make no apologies, then, for the book itself. A good many chapters of this book have circulated in the programming underground for some time along with notes taken from my courses. It seemed to be an opportune time to make the outlines of this new methodology available to a broad spectrum of interested people. Certainly, this book will not satisfy everyone; however, I hope it will stimulate people to think more deeply about some of the concepts that we have found so successful. If you have made it this far (assuming you haven't skipped the meat of the book), you will probably have some notions about my beliefs. Before you judge the book, try the approach. Apply it to the hardest problem you can find, and see if it doesn't help. Not everything that I have said here is likely to excite you. Use what you like, and think about the rest.

In case the point has escaped you, the book is really about applying logic to solving systems problems — everything else is secondary. Occasionally, when I reread one of Warnier's books, I am driven to pull out my dog-eared texts on set theory and mathematical logic. I don't expect you to do the same, at least not initially, but be assured that it's all there, if you just know where to look for it and how to apply it. That mathematical underpinning is both a tremendous strength and a minor weakness. We know, for example, that what we are developing has to work. On the other hand, we recognize that many people will rebel at the amount of work needed to do it right, especially if they consider systems development and programming to be an art.

It has been said with considerable justification that data processors are unsuccessful in dealing with human factors in systems analysis and development. In recent years, many systems professionals have taken a keener interest in the relationships between the systems that are being developed and the people who use them. Surprisingly, many of the most significant gains have been the result of other improvements in systems technology. The increased emphasis in structured systems design upon the logical systems requirements has had considerable beneficial fallout in terms of improving relations with users. In many cases, users now feel that the systems analyst is worrying more about the user's problem and less about the computer.

Moreover, one of the major advantages of Warnier Diagrams has been the ease with which they communicate to people who are not specifically trained in data processing. This alone represents a major breakthrough. For years, we have been attempting to build programs that were easier for people to understand; however, most of our attempts seemed directed at adding new features to programming languages and operating systems, without greatly improving understandability. When we begin to concentrate on structuring our logic, the problem of writing understandable, maintainable programs becomes considerably easier.

The next generation of systems professionals will be able to take advantage of many tools that the first two or three generations did not have. They, too, will have the benefit of an organized, disciplined body of knowledge relating to the problems that they face. In time, they also will have automated tools with which to work. I am amazed and a little stunned by the productivity and quality of some of the young people who are beginning to work in systems and are trained only in these new techniques. The break between the old and new ways is already dramatic, and will become even more so.

The next two books planned for this series, *Structuring Data* and *Data Structured Programming,* are both aimed at filling a gap in the computing literature, and bridging the separation of logical problems from the more physical aspects of systems development and of programming. In essence, structured systems design is a discipline founded upon logical, mathematical principles. If we fully understand the problem and can state it correctly, then we have reason to believe that we can solve it. This is equally true, whether talking about the design of a data base, of a system, or of a program. Computer systems, for example, do nothing other than what we tell them — that is their great strength. But telling them to do the right things involves understanding clearly and precisely what the right things actually are. The future books in this series will address some of the guidelines of designing data structures and programs that do exactly what is required.

I have not attempted to deal at any length with the management questions raised by the introduction of structured systems design into an organization. If you are particularly interested, I would recommend Ed Yourdon's *How to Manage Structured Programming* (New York: YOURDON inc., 1976). While many of the approaches he discusses are different from those of structured systems design, the philosophy is much the same, and so, too, is the basic management problem — the management of change. However, change will not just happen. There are, in the general scheme of things, those managers who seem to take advantage of new technologies as they appear, and those who never seem to quite get around to using them, because they are too busy putting out fires!

We have just begun to study the application of structured thinking to the organization of projects. After all, a good plan is a program that gets the right set of actions done on the right set of things at the right times. Order is all important. Things done out of order usually have to be done over, sometimes two, three, and even four times. The truly successful manager does the right things in the right sequence. That means that he doesn't have to backtrack often. Slowly, we are learning how to manage the analysis, design, development, and maintenance of information systems.

The finishing touches to this book were done a month or so following a conference of structured systems design users in Topeka. The word at that meeting was that structured systems design and development are working, in some cases better than we had any reason to expect. But that does not mean there are no more problems. In fact, what we concluded was that structured systems design simply opened up a whole new realm of problems to face: problems of how to get users to define the right problem; problems of how to get the systems analyst to be exact in his definition of problems to the programmer; problems of how to accurately estimate and manage large-scale systems efforts. We don't have the answers, not all of them at any rate, but we're getting there.

APPENDIX A
SYSTEMS DESIGN LANGUAGE
(SDL)

APPENDIX B
STRUCTURED FLOWCHARTS

```
┌─────────────────────────────────────────┐
│                                         │
│        MODULE (logic block)             │
│                                         │
├─────────────────────────────────────────┤
│                                         │
│   Module-name                           │
│                                         │
│           BEGIN module-name             │
│                                         │
│               statement,                │
│                     .                   │
│                     .                   │
│                     .                   │
│                                         │
│           END [module-name]             │
│                                         │
│                                         │
└─────────────────────────────────────────┘
```

Example

```
PROGRAM-X
    BEGIN PROGRAM-X
        DO BEGIN-X
        DO PROCESS-X UNTIL ALL-DATA-PROCESSED
        DO END-X
    END-PROGRAM-X
```

```
┌─────────────────────────────────────┐
│                                     │
│           ALTERNATION               │
│                                     │
├─────────────────────────────────────┤
│                                     │
│     IF condition                    │
│        THEN                         │
│              true-statements        │
│        [ELSE                        │
│              false-statements]      │
│     END-IF  [condition]             │
│                                     │
│                                     │
└─────────────────────────────────────┘
```

Example

```
IF PATIENT-ACTIVE
    THEN
        DO COMPUTE-AND-PRINT-BILL
    ELSE
        SKIP
END-IF
```

```
┌─────────────────────────────────────────┐
│                                         │
│        ALTERNATION (MULTIPLE)           │
│                                         │
├─────────────────────────────────────────┤
│     CASE condition-class                │
│         WHEN condition₁                 │
│             statement₁                  │
│         [WHEN condition₂                │
│             statement₂                  │
│                                         │
│                    .                    │
│                    .                    │
│                    .                    │
│                                         │
│         WHEN conditionₙ                 │
│             statementₙ                  │
│         ELSE                            │
│             statementₙ₊₁]               │
│     END CASE                            │
│                                         │
└─────────────────────────────────────────┘
```

CASE condition-class

    WHEN $condition_1$

        $statement_1$

    [WHEN $condition_2$

        $statement_2$

          .
          .
          .

    WHEN $condition_n$

        $statement_n$

    ELSE

        $statement_{n+1}$]

END CASE

Example

```
CASE TYPE
    WHEN TYPE = "A"
        DO TYPE-A-PROCESSING
    WHEN TYPE = "B"
        DO TYPE-B-PROCESSING
    WHEN TYPE = "D"
        DO TYPE-D-PROCESSING
    ELSE
        DO ERROR PROCESSING
END-CASE
```

```
┌─────────────────────────────────────────────────────────┐
│                                                         │
│          REPETITION (TYPE-1)                            │
│                                                         │
├─────────────────────────────────────────────────────────┤
│                      ⎧  WHILE  ⎫                        │
│     DO [name]*       ⎨         ⎬      condition         │
│                      ⎩  UNTIL  ⎭                        │
│                                                         │
│            statements₁                                  │
│                     .                                   │
│                     .                                   │
│                     .                                   │
│                                                         │
│         END-DO                                          │
│                                                         │
└─────────────────────────────────────────────────────────┘
```

Examples

1.   DO REGION-PROCESSING UNTIL ALL-DATA-PROCESSED

2.   DO UNTIL ALL-DATA-PROCESSED
            DO GET-NEXT-TRANSACTION
            DO CALCULATE-RETIREMENT
            DO PUT-RETIREMENT-RECORD
     END-DO

---

*If "name" is present, the END-DO is omitted; and if the "name" is omitted, then the END-DO must be present.

```
┌─────────────────────────────────────────────────────────┐
│                                                         │
│   REPETITION (TYPE-2)                                   │
│                                                         │
├─────────────────────────────────────────────────────────┤
│                                                         │
│                        ⎧ EACH ⎫                         │
│   DO [name} FOR  ⎨       ⎬ logical-element(s)            │
│                        ⎩ ALL  ⎭                         │
│                                                         │
│       statements₁                                       │
│               .                                         │
│               .                                         │
│               .                                         │
│                                                         │
│   END-DO                                                │
└─────────────────────────────────────────────────────────┘
```

Examples

1. DO REGION-PROCESSING FOR EACH REGION

2. DO FOR EACH TRANSACTION
        DO GET-TRANSACTION
        DO LOOK-UP-VALUE
        IF VALUE > RANGE
            THEN
                DO REPORT-ERROR
            ELSE
                DO PROCESS-TRANSACTION
        END-IF
    END-DO

3. DO FOR ALL EMPLOYEES
        DO CALCULATE-AND-PRINT-SALARY
    END-DO

REPETITION (TYPE-3)

DO [name] FOR {do-variable = initial-value $\left\{\begin{matrix} TO \\ , \end{matrix}\right\}$

test-value $\left[\left\{\begin{matrix} BY \\ , \end{matrix}\right\} \text{ increment}\right]\Big\}$

    statement,
       .
       .
       .

END-DO

Example

```
DO FOR I = 1, 10
    MOVE A TO B (I)
    COMPUTE A = C + B (I) + 2
END-DO
```

```
┌─────────────────────────────────┐
│                                 │
│          INVOCATION             │
│                                 │
├─────────────────────────────────┤
│                                 │
│          [DO] name              │
│                                 │
│                                 │
└─────────────────────────────────┘
```

Examples

1.   DO PROCESS-PAYROLL

2.   DO BEGIN-X
     DO PROCESS-X
     DO END-X

3.   GET NEXT TRANSACTION

NULL STATEMENT
SKIP

Example

IF PAST-DUE

    THEN

        DO PRODUCE-PAST-DUE-NOTICE

    ELSE

        SKIP

END-IF

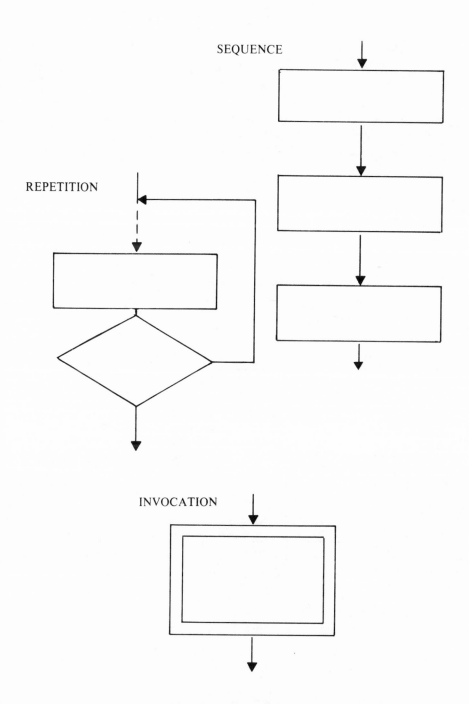

SEQUENCE

REPETITION

INVOCATION

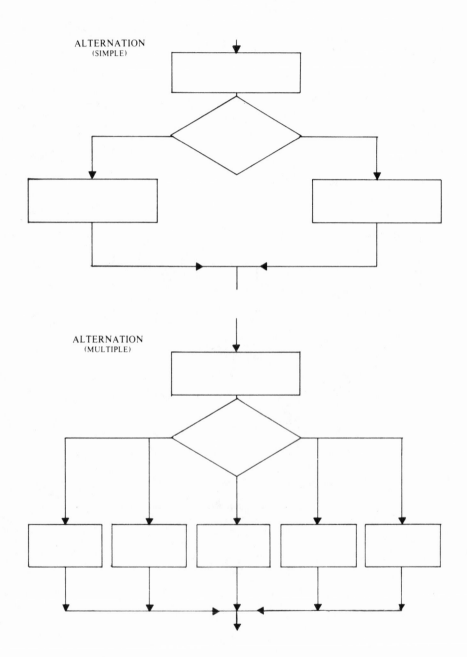

ALTERNATION
(SIMPLE)

ALTERNATION
(MULTIPLE)

BIBLIOGRAPHY

Bachman, C.W. "Data Structure Diagrams," *Data Base,* Vol. 1, No. 2 (Summer 1969).

Bertini, M.T., and Y. Tallineau. *Le COBOL Structure: Un Modèle de Programmation.* Paris: Editions d'Informatique, 1974.

A description of coding Logical Construction of Programs (L.C.P.)-designed solutions in a structured COBOL.

Caine, S., and E.K. Gordon. "P.D.L. — A Tool for Software Design," *AFIPS Proceedings of 1975 National Computer Conference.* Vol. 44, pp. 271-276. Montvale, N.J.: AFIPS Press, 1975.

A description of the use of a program design language (P.D.L.) to aid in the systematic development of structured programs.

Jackson, M.A. *Principles of Program Design.* New York: Academic Press, 1975.

A discussion of a programming methodology very similar in many respects to Warnier's L.C.P.

Kernighan, B.W., and P.J. Plauger. *Elements of Programming Style.* New York: McGraw-Hill, 1974.

Neely, P.M. *Fundamentals of Programming.* Lawrence, Kan.: University of Kansas Computation Center, 1973.

This was one of the first books to use Warnier's methodology in conjunction with structured programming.

_____, and K.T. Orr. "A Home-Handyman's Guide to Structured Programming in COBOL." Paper delivered for Langston, Kitch & Associates, Inc., Topeka, 1975.

Orr, K.T. "Structured Systems Design." Student handouts for Langston, Kitch & Associates, Inc., Topeka, 1975.

These handouts show the development of structured systems technology. Included are a variety of examples of the use of Warnier Diagrams, HIPO/DB charts, structured narratives, and structured COBOL.

――――. "Structured Systems Design — Documentation Guidelines." Prepared for Langston, Kitch & Associates, Inc., Topeka, 1975.

These guidelines were developed to describe the approach to documenting structured systems efforts. Included are examples of the use of Warnier Diagrams, HIPO/DB charts, and SDL.

Taylor, B., and S.C. Lloyd. "DUCHESS — A High Level Information System," *AFIPS Proceedings of 1974 National Computer Conference.* Vol. 43, pp. 35-41. Montvale, N.J.: AFIPS Press, 1974.

One of the first articles on the development of a structured data base management system. The paper describes the methodology of structured organization and utilization of data.

――――. "Implementation of the DUCHESS Data Base Structure." Paper delivered at Duke University, Durham, N.C., 1975.

A further description of the use of structured data base methodology employed in the DUCHESS system.

Warnier, J.D. *L'Organization des Données d'Un Système.* Paris: Les Editions d'Organization, 1974.

This book on the application of L.C.P. to the construction of a systems data base is a start toward the building of a systems science.

_____. *Logical Construction of Programs.* 3rd ed., trans. B.M. Flanagan. New York: Van Nostrand Reinhold Co., 1976.

The only volume of Warnier's work in English. This book expounds Warnier's L.C.P. methodology in a very careful manner. While the book does not adopt structured programming directly, the programs developed are clearly well structured.

_____. *La Transformation des Programmes.* Paris: Les Editions d'Organization, 1975.

In this book, Warnier develops a method of modifying and maintaining well-structured L.C.P. programs.

_____, and B. Flanagan. *Entrainment à la Programmation.* Vols. I-II. Paris: Les Editions d'Organization, 1972.

These two volumes represent a statement of Warnier's L.C.P. methodology. This methodology, relating the development of logical data structured programs, is one keystone of structured systems design.

Yourdon, E. *How to Manage Structured Programming.* New York: YOURDON inc., 1976.

A discussion of the management problems encountered by introducing structured techniques to existing organizations. The book describes methods for beginning in a manner that is likely to prove successful.

_____, and L. Constantine. *Structured Design.* New York: YOURDON inc., 1975.

INDEX